EFFECTS
OF PHYSICAL ACTIVITY
ON CHILDREN

A SPECIAL TRIBUTE TO MABEL LEE

American Academy
of Physical Education Papers
No. 19

EFFECTS
OF PHYSICAL ACTIVITY
ON CHILDREN

A SPECIAL TRIBUTE TO MABEL LEE

American Academy
of Physical Education Papers
No. 19

Fifty-seventh Annual Meeting
Atlanta, Georgia
April 15–16, 1985

Published by Human Kinetics Publishers, Inc.,
for the American Academy of Physical Education

Editors

G. Alan Stull
Helen M. Eckert

Academy Seal designed by
R. Tait McKenzie

ISBN 0-87322-049-8
ISSN 0741-4633

Printed in the United States of America

Copies of this publication may be ordered from:
Human Kinetics Publishers, Inc.
Box 5076, Champaign, IL 61820
(217) 351-5076

CONTENTS

Introduction

G. Alan Stull
University of Wisconsin–Madison

Included in this volume of *The Academy Papers* are 10 review articles summarizing existing research on the effects of exercise on factors such as moral, social, emotional, intellectual, and physical development; weight control; physical fitness; motor learning; and coronary risk factors in children. The articles have been carefully researched and provide an up-to-date synthesis of the research dealing with the effects of physical activity on children.

Although not scientifically supported, literature throughout history is replete with references attesting to the importance of the early years in determining lifestyle during adulthood. For example, in verse 6, chapter 2 of the Old Testament Book of Proverbs it is written, "Train up a child in the way he should go; and when he is old, he will not depart from it." In 1671, in his famous *Paradise Regained,* John Milton wrote, "The childhood shows the man, as morning shows the day." Although those references deal primarily with moral virtues, research literature available today would indeed suggest that one's childhood years are important in determining attitudes and habits in later life, including those relating to exercise. Thus, the papers contained in this volume deal with an extremely critical time in the human life span and represent a vital segment of the research literature in physical education.

Unfortunately, much of the popular literature one reads today dealing with the effects of exercise on children is based more on emotion than on scientific fact. It is also contradictory. One reads about the benefits the child may accrue from participating in vigorous exercise or perhaps some form of exercise program that is currently popular or which the author may be advocating. At the other end of the continuum are authors who claim that the undesirable effects of vigorous activity and children's sport may far outweigh their benefits.

Fortunately, the past decade has seen a marked increase in the amount of research devoted to the effects of participation in vigorous exercise and sport by children. One generalization that can be drawn from this research is that such participation is neither inherently good nor inherently bad; rather, its value is dependent upon the quality of the experience, which in turn may be influenced by a wide range of factors. These would include but would not be limited to such considerations as the social readiness, emotional maturity, skill level, and physical characteristics of the child, and the social demands, psychological stresses, required skill level, and physical demands of the activity.

The papers in this volume have been prepared by some of the most distinguished scholars in our field and provide a critical assessment of this very important and timely topic. It is hoped that the reader will find the volume both interesting and informative.

Also included here is the paper presented by Betty Spears at the first Mabel Lee Luncheon. Miss Lee was the third president of the Academy and the first woman to hold that office. A former president of the American Physical Education Association, a noted author, and an individual who has spent nearly seven decades as a professional physical educator, Miss Lee was present at the Atlanta meetings and responded at the conclusion of the address by Dr. Spears. Unfortunately, Miss Lee's remarks are not available for publication, but Dr. Spears' article is a carefully researched and extremely informative summary of Miss Lee's long and very distinguished career.

A Tribute to Mabel Lee

Betty Spears
Professor Emerita, University of Massachusetts–Amherst

Miss Lee is a woman of many firsts. Not only was she the first woman president of the Academy, but also the first woman president of the American Physical Education Association. And she was president of the Association of Directors of Physical Education for Women in Colleges and Universities, one of two forerunners of the National Association for Physical Education in Higher Education. She is a truly remarkable physical educator. She has been honored by professional organizations, educational institutions, and civic groups. Miss Lee is a renowned professional colleague who carries a torch for the highest ideals of physical education.

Today we celebrate a professional life of service, love, and great heart. What manner of woman is Mabel Lee? She is a gentlewoman who, several years ago when she was a young 93, called the federal government "all wet" (Hawkins, 1979) in its interpretation of equality for girls and boys in sport. She is resolute and dauntless in her quest to make the benefits of physical education available to all. Her great personal integrity, her love of physical education, her intellectual achievements, her organizational ability, her zest for life, and her lively sense of humor mark her as an uncommon woman. She has been and is at peace with herself, accepting her many achievements and her few disappointments from the commanding perspective of 98 years of a good life.

Interestingly, Miss Lee is 1 year younger than the American Alliance for Health, Physical Education, Recreation, and Dance, which is celebrating its 100th anniversary this year. As you all know, the association held its organizational meeting in Brooklyn, New York, in 1885. A year later, in Clearfield, Iowa, on August 18, Mabel Lee was born. The life of the senior stateswoman of physical education almost parallels that of our national professional organization. Her decision to become a physical educator was influenced by her home and her education.

Mabel was the second of four daughters—Ferne, Mabel, Jean, and Madge. When she was about 7, the family moved to Centerville, Iowa, where the Lee girls grew up in typical small-town fashion. In her delightful memoirs, *Memories of a Bloomer Girl* (1977), she recounts her happy, secure childhood and strong family life which laid the foundation for her great personal integrity. Somewhat frail and underweight, young Mabel did not permit these limitations to interfere with her love of games and physical activities. Miss Lee was graduated from the local high school and then became one of the very few young women in the United States to enter college.

The Lees' decision to educate their girls beyond the local high school was extraordinary. In 1904 only 2% of the nation's youth attended college, and of that small number only .5% were women. When the Lees sought a suitable college for their daughters,

Iowa boasted of state universities and private colleges such as Iowa Wesleyan, Grinnell College, and Coe, a small coeducational college with strong religious traditions. Mabel and her sister Ferne entered Coe College in the fall of 1904.

With a double major in psychology and philosophy, and a minor in biology, Miss Lee found time to revel in an exciting new subject called *physical education*. More importantly, she met Charlotte Poyneer, the women's physical education teacher, who had been a student at the Boston Normal School of Gymnastics. By December of her freshman year, Miss Lee knew what career she wished to follow. After discussing her future with her parents, it was decided that she would complete her degree at Coe and then enroll in the Boston Normal School of Gymnastics where Miss Poyneer had received her professional training.

While Miss Poyneer may have talked to Mabel Lee generally about education in Boston and specifically about education at the Boston Normal School of Gymnastics, she could not have foreseen the impact the school and its director, Amy Morris Homans, would make on her life. Miss Homans not only prepared gymnastics teachers but also educated women to become directors of physical education to fill the positions rapidly opening in colleges and universities. She expected her students to excel both in and out of the classroom. She made sure that her students acquired the proper social graces, were well groomed and, above all, were "womanly." For Miss Homans, womanliness did not mean being pale, passive, and submissive but rather healthy, well mannered, well groomed, and competent to conduct physical education programs. Admission to the Boston Normal School of Gymnastics was very competitive. Each fall about 50 students arrived, and within a month about half had been dismissed.

Mabel Lee can attest to the probation period. She arrived in Boston somewhat frail, as she had been most of her life. Miss Homans believed the new student from Iowa lacked sufficient vigor and *ordered* her to gain 10 pounds in 6 weeks or leave. It was not easy! Glasses of milk between classes, rest and more rest, more milk and, perhaps more than anything, perseverance. As would happen over and over in her professional life, Miss Lee did not give up when facing difficulties. Gain weight she did! She acknowledged a new sense of well-being and settled in to learn all she could from her new school. During this period the Boston Normal School of Gymnastics affiliated with Wellesley College, just west of Boston. The Class of 1910, Mabel Lee's class, had the benefits of a year in Boston and a year at Wellesley. In Boston, Miss Lee especially enjoyed gymnastics under Dr. Collin and the courses taught by professors from Harvard University, Harvard Medical School, and the Massachusetts Institute of Technology. At Wellesley she marveled at the beauty of the campus and reveled in the new gymnasium and laboratories fitted with the latest equipment.

Upon graduation Miss Lee became part of the long line of women physical education teachers who had been students of Amy Morris Homans. At that time outstanding alumnae included Senda Berenson, Ethel Perrin, J. Anna Norris, Helen McKinstry, Marjorie Bouvé, Winifred Van Hagen, and Blanche Trilling. These women carried with them Miss Homans' beliefs in the highest ideals of physical education and an almost missionary zeal to improve the health and well-being of women and children as a means of ensuring "the good life" for future generations. Miss Lee left Wellesley well prepared in physical education and with a high regard for Miss Homans, her school, and her ideals, or as we might say, her philosophy of physical education.

Throughout her professional career Miss Lee held the coveted title of director of physical education for women—at Coe College, Oregon Agricultural College, and Beloit. In 1924 she accepted the position she held until retirement—Professor and Director of Physical Education for Women at the University of Nebraska in Lincoln. In each position she conducted physical education programs based on the tenets instilled in her by Miss Homans. Along with other women physical educators of the period, she staunchly supported physical examinations with follow-up programs if necessary, gymnastics, exercise, dance, and sport. For these women, physical education was not just for the highly skilled athlete but also for the dub, the student with poor posture, the frail student, the athletic misfit and, above all, the *average* college woman. The overriding emphasis on providing physical education for all students encouraged instructional and intramural programs and discouraged intercollegiate athletics for women. One of Miss Lee's early research projects underscores this point of view.

In 1922 Miss Lee agreed to take part in a debate on intercollegiate athletics for women at the meeting of the Middle West Society of College Directors of Physical Education for Women. Assigned the position *against* intercollegiate athletics, she gathered data from questionnaires sent to 50 colleges and universities in 23 states. When she arrived at the meeting she discovered that the woman speaking *for* intercollegiate athletics could not attend and that she was expected to present both sides of the issue. Miss Lee's two-sided debate with herself became the now classic, "The Case For and Against Intercollegiate Athletics for Women."

The information from the questionnaires was carefully tallied and percentages were computed. Seventy-eight percent of the institutions reporting did not support intercollegiate athletics for women, but 22% did; 48% of the institutions believed that women would not benefit physically from intercollegiates, 24% believed that they would benefit, 4% were in doubt, and 24% did not express an opinion. The most frequently reported reason for not approving intercollegiate athletics for women was the fear that the average college woman who would benefit from physical education would be neglected (Lee, 1923, 1931). The majority of women physical educators did not waver from that position for 50 years.

Perhaps Miss Lee's own experiences supported this strong philosophic position. She loved sport and dance but never considered herself a star athlete. She enjoyed a good precision drill in gymnastics, an exciting game of field hockey, and a twirl around the dance floor. She became a devoted hiker and, in the summer of 1922, hiked 80 miles of New England's Long Trail. Later she hiked and climbed in the Rocky Mountains and the Swiss Alps and enjoyed canoe trips on the border lakes in Minnesota.

From 1926 to 1938 Miss Lee held the presidencies of three prestigious national organizations, all in their formative years. We sometimes forget the modest beginnings of these associations. In 1918, Miss Lee attended the second meeting of the Middle West Society of College Directors of Physical Education for Women in Ann Arbor, Michigan. Just imagine eight women, the entire attendance, meeting in a rooming-house bedroom. As one of the younger members, Miss Lee sat on the floor.

Fewer than 20 women were present in 1924 when the Middle West Society joined with the Eastern and Western Societies to form the National Association of Directors of Physical Education for Women in Colleges and Universities. As you might expect, Miss Lee was one of those women. Limited to women directors in 4-year colleges and universities, the association provided a forum for discussing problems relating directly to women's physical education. As president of the group in 1926-27, Miss Lee worked to unite the district societies into a strong national organization and opened the membership to include the directors of 4-year normal schools and teachers colleges as well as those from colleges and universities. Later the association expanded and became the National Association for Physical Education of College Women.

In those days the women directors met just prior to the district meetings of the American Physical Education Association. After their meeting the women proceeded to the district association, and in this way became acquainted with problems and issues beyond those normally encountered by women. In 1928 Miss Lee found herself caught up in her district association, the Middle West Society of Physical Education. Unknown to her and much to her consternation, she had been named vice-president of the association. Miss Lee learned that the role ordinarily was assigned to a woman, and then President Lauren Post informed her that she would have nothing to do. Such a situation did not appeal to Miss Lee, but with her unerring instinct for doing the correct thing, she did nothing. At other professional meetings that winter she learned of the growing discontent between the budding district associations and the national organization, which at that time numbered only a few thousand members.

Imagine Miss Lee's feelings when she was informed of Mr. Post's sudden death, which left her president of the Middle West Society of Physical Education. As vice-president she had had nothing to do and now, as president, she discovered that there were no records to follow. Such a situation might have bewildered and discouraged many persons, but not Mabel Lee! Remember the 10 pounds to be gained at the Boston Norman School of Gymnastics? The situation became a challenge to her, an obstacle to be overcome. She resolved to keep her officers informed of the association's business so that no one in the future would face the dilemma in which she found herself.

As president of a district association, she attended the next national council meeting and found herself nominated for the vice-presidency, another office which "had been handed around among the women for many years as a polite gesture, with the presidency, that holy of holies, reserved exclusively for the men" (Lee, 1978, p. 99). As vice-president, Miss Lee served on the national council and supported President Fritz Maroney's plans to reorganize the association. When Mr. Maroney made casual references to her as the next national president, she laughed with her usual good humor and considered the remarks trifling. Mr. Maroney was not joking, however. On December 30, 1930, at the business meeting of the American Association of Physical Education council, Carl Schrader nominated Mabel Lee to be the next president. She was unanimously elected, becoming the first woman president.

By that time in her mid-40s with 20 years experience as a director of women's physical education, she had proved herself an able administrator, a woman who had overcome personal and professional adversities, and a recognized author. Further, Miss Lee was also attractive and charming. She brought to the presidency her great integrity and her high personal ideals for physical education. Her excellent sense of organization, her ability to analyze and solve problems, and her insistence that the association business be conducted in a democratic manner benefited the organization. Miss Lee completed the reorganization begun under Mr. Maroney, emphasizing the national aspects of the association. She also guided the unofficial Women's Athletic Section to its long-desired official section status and assisted in organizing a section on dance. By the end of her term she had earned the respect and admiration of national leaders in physical education as well as the titles of "Our First Lady," and "Our Mabel."

A year after Miss Lee was elected president of APEA, she became Academy Number 30. In 1931 the 29 charter fellows elected five new members—No. 30, Mabel Lee, followed by Emil Rath, Frederick W. Cozens, N.P. Neilson, and Frank S. Lloyd. By

1938, 40 members had been elected to the Academy. President R. Tait McKenzie guided the small, closely knit group through its early years. In the late 1930s, however, there was some question as to whether he should continue in the presidency. He agreed to remain in office if Miss Lee would be his vice-president. On April 28, 1938, just 7 days after the Academy meeting, Dr. McKenzie died of a heart attack, leaving Miss Lee as acting president. In 1941 she became the first woman to be elected president of the Academy.

During the 1930s Miss Lee had resolved to do something about the lack of adequate resources for physical education programs for children and women. In 1937 she published *The Conduct of Physical Education*, an important contribution to the professional literature. Her ideas speak convincingly to the 1985 theme of the American Academy of Physical Education. She calls attention to the right of every child to adequate physical and medical examinations and follow-up care, a supportive and caring home, and education for a responsible adulthood. Miss Lee (1937) asserts that "physical education has been a leader in the movement for the development of the individual according to his own needs and capacities" (p. 8). Programs should be planned for all students—handicapped and restricted children as well as highly skilled boys and girls. Her program for children consists of athletic games, rhythmical activities, stunts and tumbling, and corrective exercises if necessary. To her, the fun and joy of physical activities are vital. Her generalizations regarding physical activity for children are remarkably contemporary.

In 1939, after an amazingly productive period in her life, Miss Lee received an honorary degree from her alma mater, Coe College. Her citation (Walsh, 1939) recognized her as "an organizer and administrator of all that is best and most enduring in the field of physical education for women" (p. 106). In her writings Miss Lee calls herself a "late bloomer" (1977, p. 358). At age 52 she had served as president of three professional associations, published an important text, and received an honorary degree. I wonder what would have happened if she had been an early bloomer?

In 1952 Miss Lee retired from the University of Nebraska. Her professional and personal integrity appears only to have strengthened. During the 42 years of her professional career she never wavered from her philosophy of physical education. She continued to champion the rights of all children and women to have access to physical and medical examinations, corrective programs, and instruction in a wide variety of sport and dance activities. She believed that the highly skilled woman athlete would find a way to fill her need for physical activity, but that the average woman required a well-planned instructional and recreational program to benefit from physical education. Officially retired, lively and enthusiastic Mabel Lee moved on to other professional adventures.

Miss Lee remained in Lincoln, Nebraska, and soon undertook a major project, the preservation of our heritage. As 1960 approached, she wrote to the president of the American Association for Health, Physical Education, and Recreation inquiring about plans for the association's 75th anniversary and soon found herself fully involved. She organized many of the memorable programs of the 1960 convention in Miami and, with Bruce Bennett, prepared the 75th Anniversary issue of the *Journal of Health, Physical Education, and Recreation* (April, 1960).

The association's president, Minnie L. Lynn, appointed Miss Lee to be the association's first archivist. Miss Lee went about her task with characteristic thoroughness. She developed guidelines for the preservation of historical records, searched for lost documents, and began an inventory of the association's collection of records and materials. She delved more and more into the history of physical education. With an Amy Morris Homans Fellowship from Wellesley College she wrote her delightful autobiographies (Lee, 1977, 1978). In 1983, at the age of 97, she published a textbook, *A History of Physical Education and Sports in the U.S.A.* Her history is told through the eyes of a participant who helped shape physical education in the United States and whose professional life parallels that of the national organization for physical education.

Today, Miss Lee, we pay tribute to your steadfast belief in the benefits of physical education, your leadership in professional associations, your efforts to preserve our heritage, and your zest for life. You are a distinguished colleague and a beloved friend. Your books are dedicated to the torchbearers of the past and those of the future. *You* are a torchbearer of the present. For over seven decades you have carried a torch for the highest ideals of physical education. We thank you for your gifts of service, leadership, and love. It is a privilege for the American Academy of Physical Education to pay tribute to you, Academy No. 30, Mabel Lee!

REFERENCES

HAWKINS, L. (1979, August 20). Lee to be first Nebraskan inducted by Iowa Hall of Fame. *Lincoln Star,* p.1.

LEE, M. (1923-1924). The case for and against intercollegiate athletics for women and the situation as it stands today. *Bulletin,* Mary Hemenway Alumnae Association, Graduate Dept. of Hygiene and Physical Education, Wellesley College.

LEE, M. (1924). The case for and against....*Mind and Body,* **30,** 245-256.

LEE, M. (1931). The case for and against....*American Physical Education Review,* **29,** 13-19. (revised)

LEE, M. (1931). The case for and against....*Research Quarterly,* **2,** 93-127.

LEE, M. (1937). *The conduct of physical education.* New York: A.S. Barnes.

LEE, M. (1960, April). *Journal of Health, Physical Education and Recreation,* **31.** (75th Anniversary Issue)

LEE, M. (1977). *Memories of a bloomer girl.* Washington: American Alliance for Health, Physical Education, and Recreation.

LEE, M. (1978). *Memories beyond bloomers.* Washington: American Alliance for Health, Physical Education, and Recreation.

LEE, M. (1983). *A history of physical education and sports in the U.S.A.* New York: John Wiley.

WALSH, E.B. (1939). Wellesley in the world. *Wellesley Magazine,* **24,** 103-106.

Children and the Research Process

David H. Clarke
University of Maryland

It was most appropriate that the Academy select a concern for the study of children as the theme for this conference, held in conjunction with the Alliance's centennial celebration. One could view such a celebration as a rebirth, and thus certainly an appropriate time to consider the many important aspects of concern for the young child and the developing individual in the study of human movement. This is an era of increased sophistication in sport, a proliferation of sporting opportunity and, with the Olympic celebration every 4 years, encouragement to develop a high level of physical ability. At the Academy's 1984 Annual Meeting the focus was on the limits of human performance and the center of that discussion was, quite appropriately, the mature performer. But there has been a continuing interest in examining young athletes and individuals who may be described as preathletes. Whether the ultimate aim of research is to predict future outstanding performers among boys and girls, or simply to examine some of the conditions leading to athletic success, the Academy accepts the challenge to examine this important field.

The present era is unprecedented in the number of opportunities for sport and athletic participation for individuals of all ages. Professionals in physical education have sometimes decried the accompanying emphasis on athletics, but this has not deterred the widespread growth of organized sport. In fact, the tendency seems to be for high-level coaching to take place in individual sports outside the public school environment, some of the most advanced instruction occurring in private clubs, with private coaches and tutors. It is not the purpose of this article to discuss the advantages and disadvantages of such a situation, but simply to indicate that there is little likelihood the phenomena attendant to this type of advanced training will be analyzed carefully if those involved have little background in the research process.

Therefore, it is encouraging to note the increased attention being given to the young performer by scientists in human movement and sport in recent years. These studies have provided insight into the trainability and the comparative structural, physiological, and other parameters that underlie performance. Many of these studies have examined the performer at a young age, at the peak of his or her seasonal training for sport, but the investigators have generally not intervened directly in the training itself. Rather less insight can be found concerning physical conditioning when the investigator must make use of anecdotal records and when the process of physical training may have received less emphasis than practice of the sport. A comparative analysis can be conducted of the differences between competitive and noncompetitive children, but cause and effect may remain clouded.

This is not meant as a criticism of any particular methodology, since few investigators have it within their province to train their young subjects. Most investigators have their bases of laboratory support in colleges and universities but their subjects are usually under some other auspices such as public schools, private clubs, or community sport environments. However, a great deal of insight can be gained from cross-sectional comparisons between children who are active and those who are not active in sports.

An additional problem has been the difficulty in providing longitudinal data about performance, as compared with the cross-sectional approach. This is not the only area of exercise science in which this problem occurs, of course, but since growth and development is so dynamic there is a pressing need for increased longitudinal study of populations engaged in systematic activity and exercise. As is evident in this year's Academy program, interest in the study of children spans a wide spectrum. Most of the topics covered have had similar methodological problems. Success in dealing with these questions is a challenge to all the researchers.

When we focus on the broad texture of research in children we do not lack for subject matter; some of the earliest studies on humans have revealed a concern for body structure and for growth and development. Early artisans and sculptors examined body configuration, an interest shared by early anthropologists and comparative anatomists throughout history. Eventually, anthropometry emerged as an investigative tool in human biology. Evidence of this is seen today in most of our investigations when we report body height and weight, lean body mass, and a myriad of other descriptors. We now see a transition from an interest in pure structure to one of function, and a concern for the relationship between them.

A number of growth studies have been undertaken since the early years of this century. The first ones were primarily interested in structural and morphological changes in children, and only later was physical performance included in a serious way. The Iowa Child Welfare Research Station was established in 1917 by Bird T. Baldwin (1921) to study the physical characteristics of children. A variety of anthropometric measures was included, specifically such variables as breathing capacity and some selected strength tests. As a result of this study, Howard V. Meredith and Virginia B. Knott prepared age-height-weight charts for children from birth to maturity.

The Fels Research Institute (Sontag, 1946) was established at Antioch College in 1929, its objectives being to study factors including structure, function, and behavior of children as related to heredity and environment. This was a longitudinal study in which some 300 children and their families were examined with respect to body structure, growth, and health. It involved a combination of disciplines, including medicine, anthropology, psychology, genetics, and biochemistry. The familiar average growth curves were described, and the study also examined triplets, identical twins, siblings, and unrelated children, thus permitting an understanding of the mechanics and differences in the various growth processes.

The Institute of Child Welfare at the University of California–Berkeley (Jones & Bayley, 1941) conducted three separate longitudinal investigations, in which 30 boys and 30 girls were enrolled at birth and 20 of each sex were followed to maturity. A number of measurements were taken, including hand/wrist X-rays and various psychometric data. The physical ability measurements included right and left grip strength, and push and pull strength. An interesting relationship was discovered between strength, fitness, and social status in adolescence, which was more favorable for boys than for girls.

The Wisconsin Growth Study (Rarick & Smoll, 1967) involved annual measurement of boys and girls from ages 7 through 12 and again at age 17, and included a variety of anthropometric, strength, and motor performance items. Its main intent was to examine growth trends in height, weight, physique, and motor performance.

An extremely comprehensive growth study, which included a large number of motor performance and physical variables, was the Medford, Oregon, Boys' Growth Study (Clarke, 1971). Not only were many subjects employed at ages 7 through 18 but those initially selected were followed through their high school years. Thus it was possible to construct physical and motor growth and acceleration curves and to study individual differences in structure, strength, endurance, and other motor performance factors or abilities. In addition, these factors were related to physiological maturity, sociopersonal adjustment, and scholastic aptitude and achievement. Unique to this study was the ability to contrast the various traits among boys who did and boys who did not make athletic teams competing in interscholastic sports at the upper elementary, junior high, and senior high school levels.

Yet the full focus of our research efforts should move beyond the physical or physiological changes that occur with training in children. Many other aspects can and should be pursued. If youth sport is to prosper and overcome its high dropout rate, which is estimated to be some 75% by the time the young athlete has reached high school age (Seefeldt, 1985), then one is entitled to know the sociological and psychological factors that prevail in children's sports programs.

Researchers dealing with studies involving children and adolescents face a number of problems that may not be found with adults. This sometimes makes the design of studies more complicated, or at least forces one to deal with a set of circumstances that might not be considered typical for human performance testing. Some of the factors that must be considered and resolved include the following:

1. The first is the effect of age itself on the developmental process, which produces a "growth curve" of motor development variables. This means that children of disparate ages cannot be grouped together; instead the investigator must match subjects by age or limit the selection to individuals all of the same age. Age may either be described chronologically or by some other criterion such as physiological age. When the latter criterion is chosen, there appears to be a reduction in the variability of performance, which may be desirable in some studies. Those of us who have dealt with children in the laboratory understand what teachers have been saying all along—that age in years does not describe the whole child. Therefore one must be cautious when grouping children of similar chronological ages.

2. Another problem concerns the necessity of adapting the measurement system to the appropriate size and structure to accommodate the abilities of younger subjects. Typical laboratory testing equipment is geared for the adult and often must be modified for testing those of small stature. We do have small electrode collars and small mouthpieces, but other laboratory hardware may have to be adjusted as well. Even the pull-up apparatus may have a crossbar too large for the hand of a young child. Failure in chins may be due in part to the child's inability to hang on.

3. Psychological tests need to be age-adjusted, a fact long recognized and implemented with most standardized forms. However, they require even more modification when the population sample includes some who are mentally handicapped.

4. The method of measuring body composition is being questioned because the conversion constants for body density are based on the mature adult (mostly male adult) and thus are not appropriate for prepubescent boys or girls.

5. Motivation is another problem often encountered when testing young subjects, especially when maximum performance is desired. In this situation, the younger the subject the more difficult it is to elicit a maximum effort in tests of strength, muscular endurance, and cardiovascular capacity. Special attention must be given to instructions and demonstrations, and more trials may be needed than would be typical for the older subject.

6. The selection of a control group, so important in some studies, must be done very carefully in order to have an adequate match with the experimental subjects. Consideration for age is clearly a major factor. One of the difficulties is that a given chronological age often means the birth date can be any month during a given year. This is somewhat misleading, since a fair amount of maturation can occur over 12 months. Researchers can narrow the test group to those born within a few weeks of a given date to keep this factor from confounding any main effects. If this is done, the control group must be selected in the same way. Also, it is usually desirable for the control subjects to come from the same environment and school system as the experimental subjects. If the controls are to represent a population that is relatively nonactive, care should be taken to ensure that they are willing to perform adequately on any motor performance tests.

7. Another issue that needs to be considered is that of human subject protection. Children are not the ones who sign the consent forms, yet ultimately they are the ones who must feel free to participate or not. Parents may give their consent for the child to be part of the study, and even accompany him or her to the laboratory, but the researchers still must protect their subjects. Obtaining truly informed consent is difficult where children are concerned, and special care should be taken when the tasks involve risks if all-out performance is expected in unfamiliar surroundings. Our discussions here could well lead to clarification of policies related to the issue of appropriate forms of informed consent when testing children, this testing covering the broad spectrum of methodologies available to us in the human movement field.

These, then, are some of the issues confronting us as we seek to advance knowledge in this important area. The Academy has always been devoted to fostering the pursuit of knowledge in all aspects of human movement. As President Shea stated in 1984 (Shea, 1984, p. 147), ''the Academy must explore the cutting edge of thought, behavior, and style of those in the forefront of changes relating to the art and science of human movement and physical activity.'' For my part I will urge that our annual meetings be a time for encouraging the synthesis of new knowledge and exploring topics whose very foundations are rooted in theory. Surely, our exposition of the effects of physical activity on children will not lead us only to better ways of increasing their athletic performance, but rather will help us understand some of the mechanisms underlying physical activity that affect children. This is a fundamental issue that deserves to be protected whenever the Academy meets.

This year's program continues the thematic concept embodied in the past several annual meetings, and *The Academy Papers* will reflect the theme as the central focus. The papers selected by Dr. G. Alan Stull have been eagerly awaited by all of us as we explore *The Effects of Physical Activity on Children: A Special Tribute to Mabel Lee.*

REFERENCES

BALDWIN, B.T. (1921). The physical growth of children from birth to maturity. *University of Iowa studies in child welfare,* **1**, 1.

CLARKE, H.H. (1971). *Physical and motor tests in the Medford boys' growth study.* Englewood Cliffs, NJ: Prentice-Hall.

JONES, H.E., & Bayley, N. (1941). The Berkeley growth study. *Child Development,* **12**, 167.

RARICK, G.L., & Smoll, F.L. (1967). Stability of growth in strength and motor performance from childhood to adolescence. *Human Biology, 39,* 195.

SEEFELDT, V. (1985). Why are children's sports programs controversial? *Journal of Physical Education, Recreation, & Dance,* **56**, 16.

SHEA, E.J. (1984). The future agenda. In H.M. Eckert & H.J. Montoye (Eds.), *Exercise and health.* Champaign, IL: Human Kinetics.

SONTAG, L.W. (1946). Biological and medical studies at the Samuel S. Fels Research Institute. *Child Development,* **17**, 81.

Moral Aspects
of an Education in Movement

Peter J. Arnold
Dunfermline College of Physical Education, Edinburgh

The relationship between the physical and moral life has been of philosophical and educational interest for at least 2000 years. It is therefore not surprising that the issues and problems surrounding this relationship are still with us today. They remain immense and diverse. For the purpose of this paper, however, and in order to keep matters within bounds, I will deal with the phenomenon of sport as a particular and paradigm case of "the physical."

A look at the place of sport in contemporary life and a study of the appropriate literature suggests that there are three broadly held views about the relationship between participation in sport (including games) and moral development. I shall refer to them as the positive view, the neutral view, and the negative view. The *positive view* is the belief that there is a clear, if unproven, connection between the playing of team sports and the development of social and moral values. This belief, which emanated from the English public schools of the 19th century, gave birth to two theories, both of which have continued to influence attitudes toward sport, especially in its relationship to education. The first was that participation in sport, especially in the form of team games, was educationally useful in that it led to desirable social and moral outcomes. In particular, it was thought to lead to an ability to cooperate with others on a basis of understanding and mutual respect, as well as an ability to strive to the utmost in a cause without recourse to personal bitterness or vindictive meanness. In addition, it was thought that such qualities as generosity, magnanimity, courage, and steadfastness could be cultivated and developed in sport.

The second theory was that such training could not only be provided for on the playing fields but that its effects were transferable into the world at large and could be called upon if necessary in battle or in the service of the Empire. Suffice it to say that in recent years both theories have been seriously questioned. Nonetheless, the view that sport can be used as a means of teaching social and moral values persists. Such sentiments are still enshrined in the movement known as Olympism, now regarded by many as outdated and antiquarian.

The second, or *neutral view*, arises from the conceptual cum classificatory position that sport is a form of play and that, because of its self-contained and separate nature, is discontinuous with the "business of life" and is therefore, when compared to life's concerns, morally unimportant. What goes on in sport, in other words, morally speaking, is relatively inconsequential. It is essentially nonserious rather than serious. This view considers that sport, when stripped of its trappings and manufactured importance, is only a game and is not, from the moral point of view, to be compared with such matters as poverty, pestilence, war, and famine. This neutralist view of the relationship between sport and morality is important not only because it has a respectable intellectual pedigree, but because it is embodied in at least one influential theory of education.[1] It does, however, I think, rest upon an inadequate understanding of sport and a too hasty assimilation of it into the realm of play.

The third, or *negative view,* is one that largely arises from the findings of empirical studies, which are often based upon professional or high-level competitive sport where winning is deemed of crucial importance. Such studies appear to point to the fact that not only does cheating and foul play occur, but that to be successful one must possess such traits as dominance, assertiveness, and nonsociability.[2] Futhermore, it would seem that the qualities often associated with sportsmanship, such as generosity and magnanimity, are more likely to be disregarded by high-level participants than by low-level ones.[3] Such findings are made abundantly apparent both on television and in the newspapers when coverage is given to big match events. Because of the undesirable tendencies associated with some forms and levels of competitive sport, some educationists have argued that competitive sport is antithetical to moral education, that it detracts from rather than enhances moral development (Bailey, 1975). Such "facts" about the relationship between sport and morality cannot be disregarded. On the other hand, they should not necessarily be taken as representative of the way sport is conducted in general.

A further difficulty is that a number of studies do not make it clear in what sense the terms employed are being used. The term "character" is often used as if it were interchangeable with "personality" and it is not always clear how particular traits identified in the context of a sport relate, if at all, to a person's overall dispositions or, more particularly, to his or her character in the moral sense of that term. Indeed, it would be helpful if future studies of sport in relation to character were viewed not so much through an inventory of individual actions performed as through a description of the principles that give coherence and meaning to a person's behavior and the relatively enduring motivations that underlie it.

These three views of the relationship of sport to morality are all interwoven to some extent into the educational systems of different cultures. As a result, the picture is far from clear. It is likely to vary from one country to another,[4] even from one school to another. It is not my intention to attempt a comparative study or to comment further on these varying views, but rather to look at the relationship between sport and moral development in the context of education in a conceptual way and to point out what logical (but not necessarily factual) connections there are and what should flow from them in terms providing guidelines for practice. I will begin by saying something about morality and moral education.

MORALITY AND MORAL EDUCATION

In broad terms it can be said that morality is concerned with our interpersonal relations. It involves our consideration and concern for others as well as for ourselves and it attempts to distinguish right from wrong and good from bad. Morality is therefore involved with values and principles to consider before choosing or engaging in a particular course of action. Such principles as universality or impartiality, rational benevolence, and liberty are frequently pointed to as underpinning the character of moral discourse and action. Universality implies that the principles identified must be applicable to all. Rational benevolence recognizes the importance of reason-giving as well as recognizing the interests of all so that no individual or group is wittingly favored at the expense of another. Liberty calls attention to the fact that for an act to be moral it must be free. That is to say, it is a freely chosen act and one for which the agent can be held responsible and accountable.

The term *moral education* refers to the intentional bringing about of moral growth. It is, according to Kohlberg (1971, p. 25), the encouragement of a capacity for moral judgment. More than this, it is also concerned with a disposition to act in accordance with whatever moral judgments are made. What distinguishes moral education is that it is a deliberate and intentional activity which is concerned with the cultivation of principled moral judgment and a willing disposition to act upon that judgment. Both rational autonomy and strength of will are involved here. To be able to form a moral judgment and yet not act upon it is to fall short of what moral education entails. It is when a moral judgment is translated into an appropriate moral action that moral conduct, and therefore moral education, is most clearly expressed. McIntosh (1979, p. 167) clearly had something similar in mind when he wrote,

> The morally educated person is expected not only to be able to make moral judgments but act upon them. The moral life necessitates a host of personal dispositions. The moral person must think the issue through to the limits of his capacity but if morally right action is to occur the person must be disposed to act on his moral judgment.

What differentiates moral education from moral training, the latter implying a form of drilling to get pupils to conform to moral rules without much understanding of the principles involved, is that the pupils themselves are encouraged to reflect upon moral issues in the light of fundamental moral principles and make their own rational judgments, which they then translate into appropriate moral action. An important criterion of success in moral education, writes Meakin (1982, p. 65),

> is the degree to which an individual is willing and able to subject a given set of moral rules to his or her own critical scrutiny and decide in the light of reason whether to act on these or on some self-chosen set of rules.

It might be thought, from what has been said, that it is always necessary first to think and then to act, but this is not necessarily the case. What happens quite often in practice, perhaps especially in sport, is that the players act spontaneously without reasoning out first why they act in the way they do. A morally educated person is able to display moral concern without necessarily having to reason out a course of action in advance. However, this does not mean that if challenged he or she could not justify the action by pointing to the underlying moral rules and principles by which all actions can be judged. In this respect no distinction holds between actions that take place within the framework of games and sports and actions that do not. Aspin (1975, p. 57) underlines much of what I shall be maintaining when he observes,

> Morality therefore, and *a fortiori* moral education is concerned with helping us to understand that human life is beset with obligations of one sort and another. One of its

aims will thus be to give us a knowledge of the rules which function in this particular "game" and to seek to develop in us a grasp of its underlying principles, together with the ability to apply these rules intelligently and to have the settled disposition to do so.

In connection with the development of moral character, Kant (1960), in his reflections on education, recognized there is more to education than book learning. He believed strongly that the essential thing about education is the formation of the person by his (her) own efforts in terms of that person's talents and character (pp. 2-3). The commandment to live in accordance with nature paves the way for the commandment to go beyond nature by the exercise of reason in terms of duty and law (p. 108). For Kant, the primary end of education is the development of moral character. If this is to be achieved, each pupil must not only be accorded respect by others, by being viewed as an end rather than merely as a means, but his or her self-respect must also be cultivated. When a person lies, that person has robbed himself or herself of the dignity and trust that everyone should have (p. 102). Lying, cheating. and other forms of taking advantage of another are to be regretted not only in social terms but also in terms of the moral damage this does to one's own character. It will be argued shortly that such self-damaging acts are applicable to the sphere of sport and games no less than to other spheres of life for, like other activities, they are both social and personal in nature. Lying and cheating are to be condemned just as much as honesty and fair play are to be upheld, for they affect the self-respect of the person just as they affect the quality of relations with others. Kant did not see the formation of character as something happening overnight, but rather as something that emerges from a constant and prolonged process of self-formation.

Kant's view on the relationship between education and the formation of character is important to movement in at least three respects. First, it is seen as a moral view based upon reasoned and universalizable principles. Second, it emphasizes the giving of respect to others as well as having respect for oneself. Third, it draws attention to the fact that the development of character is not a passive process but an autonomously active and purposeful one having to do with self-formation. I shall want to uphold all these points in dealing with sport and the conduct appropriate to it. Before tackling this task more specifically, however, it will be helpful to look at the ethical basis of sport, which will be depicted as a distinctive form of practice concerned with fairness.

SPORT AS FAIRNESS

The idea and practice of sport, I suggest, is concerned with justice as fairness. Rawls (1958, p. 165), in speaking of this relationship (although he is predominantly concerned with the social practice of institutions), recognizes that there is a distinction but nonetheless a connection between applying the term "fairness" to a practice and applying it to a particular action by an individual. In his book, *A Theory of Justice*, he explicates his theory of fairness by referring to two principles: freedom and equality (Rawls, 1972). I want to develop this general position of Rawls in relation to sport and demonstrate that the practice of sport is not only just but essentially (despite its breakdown from time to time) moral.

In broad terms, justice as fairness relates to sport, with regard to the principle of freedom, by an individual having the right to choose or reject a certain sport.[5] In narrow terms it relates to his or her agreeing to the rules characterizing that sport. Insofar as the individual sees his or her life and moral character bound up and coexistent with his or her choices, activities, and efforts, that person will see that sport is no less serious than other forms of human practice. The point here is that although a sport may be regarded as a particular kind of practice characterized by its rules, it is by no means separate from or discontinuous with life or moral concern. It is in fact an identifiable form of life and, like law or medicine, is not a morally irrelevant one.[6]

Similarly, the principle of equality relates to sport in that players of a particular sport come together in the full knowledge that its rules apply to themselves as well as others. They realize and agree that the rules are in the interest of *all* players and are expected to be applied impartially so that one player or team will not gain unfair advantage over another. It is on this basis that sport as a competitive practice does or should proceed. The point here is that both logically and morally there is only one way to play the game fairly—by the rules.[7] Acting unfairly arises not so much from accidental transgression of the rules as in the deliberate breaking of them. The cheat and spoilsport are so called not because they break the rules but because they break them intentionally to gain unfair advantage. To intentionally attempt to gain unfair advantage by breaking the rules is not to be in sport at all. It is to turn away from the concept and practice of sport as fair play for, as with moral duty, sport implies a constraint on the doing of foul deeds to gain an unfair advantage. More than this, it recognizes the unfairness of some acts that, although permitted by the rules, may actually contravene the spirit of the practice.[8]

Acting fairly involves more than merely following the rules; it involves also a commitment to what the rules stand for in the name of what is fair. The principle of equality in sport expects the duty of fair play to be accepted by all participants. Those who have grasped the principle will not only have adopted a common set of rules and their spirit but will also understand that it is only by practicing the rules that the aspirations and interests of others as well as their own can be realized. They will know that to recognize another player as a person one must consider and act toward that player in certain ways. This not only helps preserve sport as a practice but has clear implications for how relationships are to be conducted in terms of that practice.

PEDAGOGIC IMPLICATIONS

Sport as fairness has been discussed as if all players, whether adult or children, are rational and will conduct themselves on the field in accordance with rules which have an underlying ethical basis. It is of course unlikely that sport will ever be practiced universally in the way it should be. Too many chauvinistic and socioeconomic pressures militate against this. Nonetheless, from the pedagogic point of view it is necessary to attempt what ought to be the case. Two general points are worth making in this connection. They concern initiation into sport and the development of character.

Initiation Into Sport

Unless children are systematically made to understand the nature of the practice of sport, and the rules and principles upon which it is based, it cannot be said they have been properly initiated into it. Clearly only so much can be reasonably expected by way of understanding at different ages and stages, and it is here that Kohlberg's (1971) model of moral cognitive development is an important reference point for the physical educator.

It should be realized that understanding alone, however, even if it is at a postconventional, autonomous, and principled level—the highest of Kohlberg's stages—will not necessarily generate conduct in accordance with what is understood. As is well known, right reasoning in moral matters is not always accompanied by right conduct. Acting rightly in sport (as elsewhere) is as much a matter of caring and motivation as it is of reasoning; and unless teachers can engender through their own attitudes, beliefs, and dispositions a sense of what is understood as mattering in terms of what is practiced, there is little prospect that moral education in any full sense of that term will occur. It is important, therefore, that teachers practice what they do with skill and commitment as well as with knowledge and understanding. Accomplishing this means combating in a deliberate and planned way the Lombardian view that winning is the only thing that matters, and replacing this view with a clear conception of what constitutes "the good contest." Fraleigh (1984), in speaking of "right actions" in this context, refers to such guides as noninjurious action, mutual respect, and sympathetic regard, all of which are in keeping with the idea of moral education. Similarly, Keating (1973) and Arnold (1984), in discussing the notion of sportsmanship, point to the manner in which sport can be conducted if a knowledge of and commitment to the rules of sport are to be transformed from legalistic precepts into real interpersonal, social, and moral experience. A practical corollary to this is that the teaching and learning of "professional fouls," which are committed to overcome a threatening situation or gain a tactical advantage (that some teachers/coaches uphold as legitimate) and which incur known and predictable outcomes, should be condemned as offending the spirit of the rules and the principles upon which they are based.

Sport and the Development of Character

The second general point I wish to make is that every physical educator should in his or her professional training[9] be helped to realize that teaching sport allows the opportunity to assist in the development of moral character. If the view of sport as fairness can be accepted, then one who is concerned with the teaching of sport is ipso facto concerned with the morality of its practice. Insofar as what is fair and just and in the interests of all depends upon such admired human qualities as honesty, obedience, resolution, self-control, determination, loyalty, cooperation, and courage, so should such qualities be consciously and deliberately cultivated as a part of what is demanded by sport in order to be educated *in* it.[10] What is not being said here is that these qualities or others like them such as persistence, resourcefulness, or self-reliance are confined to sport or can only be cultivated in or through sport, or that they can necessarily be transferred and applied to other spheres of life. What is being maintained, however, is that not many activities in everyday life provide both a logical connection with morality and "the kind of opportunity or the number of them evoking the qualities which are considered desirable, as are provided by sport" (Maraj, 1965, p. 107). It is upon a proper understanding and implementation of these points that a moral education in sport depends.

NOTES

[1]See Peters (1966) and Dearden (1968, 1969).

[2]One of the best-known attacks on the assumption that sport builds character. See Ogilvie and Tutko (1971).

[3]For a helpful summary of the effects of sport on the reduction of prosocial tendencies, see Kleiber and Roberts (1981, pp. 115-116). See also Ogilvie and Tutko (1971).

[4]There is some evidence to suggest that cheating, at least at the university level of sport, is culture-specific. See Jones and Pooley (1982, pp. 19-22).

[5]The matter of whether school games should be compulsory is important because it raises the question of whether something compulsory can be justified in terms of the principle of freedom. Here I will only say, along with some educators, that it is first necessary to initiate children into an activity, albeit compulsorily, before letting them choose whether it is in their best interests to continue with it. For further comment on this point and related ones, see Arnold (1982).

[6]Two articles of interest here that touch upon the serious and nonserious aspects of play and games and have implications for sport are by Kolnai (1965-66, pp. 103-108) and Midgley (1974, pp. 231-253).

[7]This thesis has recently been challenged. See C.K. Lehman (1981).

[8]For a clear exposition of why this is so, see Fraleigh (1982).

[9]For a helpful reminder that teachers in schools are a profession and that this entails the making of ethical judgments in relation to what one is teaching, see Shea (1978).

[10]For an article that elaborates considerably upon these points and other related ones, see Arnold (1984).

REFERENCES

ARNOLD, P.J. (1982). Competitive games and education, *Physical Education Review,* **5**, 126-130.

ARNOLD, P.J. (1984). Sport, moral education and the development of character. *Journal of the Philosophy of Education,* **18**(2).

ARNOLD, P.J. (1984). Three approaches towards an understanding of sportsmanship. *Journal of the Philosophy of Sport,* **10**, 61-70.

ASPIN, D. (1975, July). Ethical aspects of sports and games. *Proceedings of the Philosophy of Education Society of Great Britain,* **9**, 49-71.

BAILEY, C. (1975). Games, winning and education. *Cambridge Journal of Education,* **5**(1), 40-50.

DEARDEN, R.F. (1968). *The philosophy of primary education.* Boston: Routledge & Kegan Paul.

DEARDEN, R.F. (1969). The concept of play. In R.S. Peters (Ed.), *The concept of education* (pp. 73-91). Boston: Routledge & Kegan Paul.

FRALEIGH, W.F. (1982, January). Why the good foul is not good enough. *Journal of Physical Education, Recreation, and Dance,* **53**, 41-42.

FRALEIGH, W.F. (1984). *Right actions in sport: Ethics for contestants.* Champaign, IL: Human Kinetics.

JONES, J.G., & Pooley, J.C. (1982). Cheating in sport: An international problem. *International Journal of Physical Education, 3,* 19-23.

KANT, E. (1960). *Education* (G.A. Churton, Trans.). Ann Arbor: University of Michigan Press.

KEATING, J.W. (1973). The ethics of competition and its relation to some moral problems in athletics. In R.G. Osterhoudt (Ed.), *The philosophy of sport* (pp. 157-176). Springfield, IL: Charles C. Thomas.

KLEIBER, D.A., & Roberts, G.C. (1981). The effects of sport experience in the development of social character: An exploratory investigation. *Journal of Sport Psychology, 3,* 114-122.

KOHLBERG, L. (1971). Stages of moral development as a basis for moral education. In C.M. Beck, B.S. Crittenden, & E.S. Sullivan (Eds.), *Moral education—Interdisciplinary approaches* (pp. 30-41). Toronto: University of Toronto Press.

KOLNAI, A. (1965-66). Games and aims. *Proceedings of the Aristotelian Society,* pp. 103-108.

LEHMAN, C.K. (1981). Can cheaters play the game? *Journal of the Philosophy of Sport, 8,* 41-46.

McINTOSH, P. (1979). *Fair play: Ethics in sport and education.* Portsmouth: NH: Heinemann.

MARAJ, J.A., (1965). Physical education and character. *Education Review, 17*(2), 103-113.

MEAKIN, D.C. (1982). Moral values and physical education. *Physical Education Review, 5*(1), 62-82.

MIDGLEY, M. (1974). The game game. *Philosophy, 49,* 231-253.

OGILVIE, B.C., & Tutko, T.A. (1971, October). Sport: If you want to build character try something else. *Psychology Today,* pp. 61-63.

PETERS, R.S. (1966). *Ethics and education.* London: Allen and Unwin.

RAWLS, J. (1958, April). Justice as fairness. *The Philosophy Review, 67*(2), 164-194.

RAWLS, J. (1972). *A theory of justice.* Oxford: Oxford University Press.

SHEA, E.J. (1978). *Ethical decisions in physical education and sport.* Springfield, IL: Charles C. Thomas.

The Effects of Physical Activity on the Social Development of Children

George H. Sage
University of Northern Colorado

There is a deep-seated and pervasive belief that the effects of involvement in physical activities extend beyond the immediate fun and excitement of the moment. Many believe that physical activities, especially play, games, and sports, provide an environment for acquiring culturally valued personal-social attitudes, values, and behaviors, and that what is learned in the physical activity setting transfers to other spheres of life. Indeed, the well-known slogan, "sport builds character" canonizes this faith in physical activities as agents of social development and is almost universally cited by community sport leaders, school officials, and parents when they are asked to justify the expenditure of vast amounts of time and money for organized sport programs.

In this paper I will deal with the socializing effects of highly organized sport for children, but also of physical activity in a broader context such as informal play. I have divided the paper into two major parts because voluntary, spontaneous play has quite different characteristics and consequences than formal, institutionalized sport. I shall first review the developmental and cognitive functions that physical activity is believed to perform in human social development, and then discuss organized sport for children and youth.

INFORMAL PLAY FORMS AND SOCIAL DEVELOPMENT

Developmental and Cognitive Functions of Physical Activity

Developmental and cognitive scientists have emphasized the function of play in the social development of children. These scholars consider children's play the crucible of social development. As part of his work on the cognitive development of children—which of course is a part of their social development—Piaget (1962, 1965) analyzed play behavior. Piaget believed that play and cognitive development are inseparable, and that each cognitive stage exhibits a unique type of play form. More important, each play form in which children engage as they pass through the various developmental stages permits them to interact in unique ways with the environment and the social actors in it. Social development therefore occurs as the child assimilates various social roles. According to Piaget, the practice of rules, the consciousness of roles, and the development of moral values, each of which is associated with play and games in the latter two developmental stages, are largely learned in the play environment and thus serve valuable functions in the larger social context (Piaget, 1965).

According to Mead (1934), the respected social psychologist whose work provided the inspiration for symbolic interactionism, play may serve as a powerful socializing agent in a child's life. A major concern of Mead's was to determine how the individual attains full development of self. It was his view that humans are the products of social interaction; he said, "The self...is essentially a social structure, and it arises in social experience" (p. 140). Inferences from Mead's ideas suggest that play and games serve important functions in the development of self in both of the general developmental stages that he elucidated, leading to self-identity.[1]

Play may contribute to the first stage because in play the child takes on and acts out roles that exist both in the immediate and in the wider social world, and in the course of acting out such roles learns to stand outside the self and thus develop a reflected view of himself or herself as a social object distinct from but related to others. Games, on the other hand, may contribute to the second stage in the development of self. In a game, the child must take the role of every player to perceive what others are doing in order to make his or her own movements. As the child learns to take the attitude of the other and permit that attitude to guide what he or she does with reference to a common end, he or she is becoming an organic member of society.

Erik Erikson (1963), whose work is generally considered within the psychoanalytic tradition, emphasized the social growth functions play may serve. Erikson proposed three stages of infantile play that are linked with his general theory of psychosexual development. In each stage the child uses play to acquire social skills. Through play the child gradually develops a sense of moral reasoning, insight into adult roles, and concern for others, as well as an ability to work cooperatively with others.

Jerome Bruner, one of the best-known contemporary cognitive psychologists, is known for his prolific research on cognitive growth and the educational process (Bruner, Jolly, & Sylva, 1976). Bruner contends that random play is the main business of infancy and childhood and is the precursor of adult competence. Play makes possible the practice of subroutines of behavior that later come together in useful problem-solving and creativity—skills that contribute to social efficiency.

Mastery Function of Physical Activity

Sigmund Freud emphasized that children act out and repeat problematic social situations in play in order to master them (Freud, 1959, 1963). According to this view, play enables children to deal with anxiety-evoking situations by allowing them to be the active masters of the situation rather than the passive victims. Freud also believed that all children aspire to adult status, so they imitate adults in their play, which enables them to master frustrating situations in childhood and adolescence. Thus do they acquire attitudes and dispositions about the social world of adults.

Games, at least the kind played in premodern societies, tend to form a bridge between voluntary, spontaneous, informal play and formal, institutionalized sport. The

---

[1]Coakley (1984) has correctly pointed out that Mead (1934) does not suggest that play and games are necessary to the process of developing a self-concept.

studies of John Roberts and his colleagues (Roberts, Arth, & Bush, 1959) comprise the most widely cited cross-cultural investigations of games, and their seminal work emphasized the social function of games in cultural mastery. In their now-classic article, "Games in Culture," Roberts et al. constructed a classification of games based on how the game's outcome is determined. Three types of games were identified: those of physical skill, those of strategy, and those of chance. Based on their analysis of ethnographic data of 50 tribal societies, and applying their three-category classification of games, they concluded that games are expressive cultural activities similar to music and folktales; moreover, they are models of various cultural activities and thus are exercises in cultural mastery. For example, games of physical skill are related to mastery of specific environmental conditions, games of strategy are related to mastery of the social system, and games of chance are related to mastery of the supernatural.

Building on this work, Sutton-Smith and Roberts (1970), in a cross-cultural study of children's games, formulated a "conflict-enculturation" theory of games to explain relationships between types of games, child-training variables, and cultural variables. In essence this theory proposed that conflict produced by specific child-rearing techniques in a culture lead to an interest and involvement in specific types of game activities that pattern this conflict in the role reversals sanctioned by the game rules. Moreover, according to Sutton-Smith (1974), "Involvement over time in these rewarding game patterns leads to mastery of behaviors which have functional value or transfer to culturally useful behavior" (p. 10).

Summary

To summarize, there is almost unanimous agreement among developmental scientists that play is important to social development. Social competence must be learned, and it is learned through social experiences; some experiences are richer in their potential for promoting social competence than others. Since much of it is social, play is particularly useful in enhancing social development. Through play, children learn how to relate to others; indeed, they learn a wide range of social skills. Play, then, is one of the keys to successful social adjustment during childhood, and it serves as a foundation for adult functioning within a society.

CHILDREN'S ORGANIZED SPORT

I shall now turn to organized sport for children and youth. I will not make the customary reference to Webb's (1969) study of the professionalization of values toward sport and the numerous studies that followed (Loy, Birrill, & Rose, 1976; Maloney & Petrie, 1972; Sage, 1980), nor will I cite the literature on sportsmanship attitudes of athletes versus nonathletes (Kistler, 1957; Richardson, 1962). There is little well-conceived and conducted research on the effects of involvement in organized sport on social development. Discrete studies analyzing the effects of physical activity involvement on a single variable, such as sportsmanship, almost trivialize the symbolic interactions that occur in a complex social setting like sport. Such an approach is much too simple to tell us anything meaningful. I want to discuss this topic from a more generic, or what might be called a sociocultural, approach, which can only be sketched out here because of limited space.

Origins of Character Development Through Sport

Long before organized sport became popular in American schools and communities, a tradition was established in England that was to have a profound influence on sporting practice in this country. This was the emergence in the mid-19th century of team sports in the British public schools (which were actually private secondary boarding schools). The games became recognized as a medium of education and they occupied a great deal of the students' time and energy (Mangan, 1981). Team sports were valued both by students and headmasters for the qualities of social character they were presumed to develop rather than for the physical exercise they provided. As McIntosh (1957) emphatically stated, "The real justification for the public school system [of sports] was sought in character training" (p. 177). In 1864 the Royal Commission on Public Schools succinctly identified the purpose of team sport by stating, "The cricket and football fields...are not merely places of exercise or amusement; they help to form some of the most valuable social qualities and manly virtues, and they hold, like the classroom and the boarding house, a distinct and important place in Public School education" (cited in McIntosh, 1957, p. 178).

It must be emphasized that the British had a social logic and attitude toward sport that made intelligible their faith in school sports for developing social traits. The games were almost totally governed by the students themselves, who organized, administered, and coached them. The games were lively and competition was spirited, but there was an emphasis on fellowship, sacrifice, cooperation, sportsmanship, and a willingness to accept defeat gracefully; there was also a sense that how one plays is a marker of how one will later behave (Mangan, 1981).

Graduates of the public schools became the leaders in many spheres of British life—in civil government, the military, domestic industry, and in commerce throughout the British Empire. They were destined to govern and control. The tradition of self-government was foundational in the English public schools because it was believed that experience in controlling oneself and governing others was good training for the future roles the boys would perform, and that is why team sports were valued so highly.

While no one in England ever attempted to empirically verify the social developmental effects of public school sports, as far as I know, faith in them was unshakable and, like so many ideas of the British upper class, sports were imported by Americans with almost no sensitivity to the profoundly different cultural conditions and circumstances. Consequently, ever since organized youth sport programs began in this country, "character development" has been universally proclaimed as an outcome. The type of character typically envisioned is the same as that envisioned by the socially elite secondary schools of 19th-century England.

Character Development in Contemporary Children's Sport

The cultural milieu and social meanings that prevailed in English public schools do not exist in America. Moreover, and perhaps more important, no serious effort has ever been made to adopt the crucial component of the English system of school sports—self-government. In fact, youth and secondary school sports in America are dominated by adult control. The self-government found in British sports is absent here. Normative rules are also vastly different. In England, accepting the role of loser when defeated in an athletic contest was considered a sign of moral maturity. In the United States, defeat is so stigmatized that fear of losing is one of the greatest stresses reported by youth sport participants (Scanlan & Lewthwaite, 1984; Scanlan & Passer, 1978, 1979). To be a gracious loser is often seen as a character flaw, or at least not something to be admired.

Uncritically abstracting a cultural form from one society and attempting to graft it onto a cultural activity of another is bad enough. Worse is the notion that sport can be reduced to a separate reality, a world of its own, disembodied from its material context. This is merely naive idealism (Gruneau, 1983). As Gruneau noted, too many apologists of sport

> lapse into forms of idealist abstraction as ways of explaining the nature and significance of sport and its role in social development....As a result....[they] have tended either to ignore or underplay the significance of material history as a part of the constituting processes of the intentions of players, and of the rules, traditions, beliefs, and organizations which define play, game, and sporting activity at different historical moments. (p. 50)

Unfortunately, this is precisely the vision of sport that is almost universally accepted in America. The conventional wisdom posits youth sport as an apolitical, democratic activity separated from ''real life,'' simply an institutionalized form of the human play impulse. The only concession to a possible social contextual role of sport is that it will make participants good citizens, loyal, willing to sacrifice for the good of the group, and courageous—that is, it will develop character.

In place of this benign view of sport's good intentions and good deeds, we need to realize that the formal and objective aspects of sport captures only a fragment of the day-to-day social relationships of the athletic experience. We need a perspective that views youth sport as an integral element in the reproduction of the prevailing structure of society. When this is done, it will be seen that organized youth sport tends to integrate participants into the existing socioeconomic system through an elective affinity between its social relations and those of contemporary American society. The structure of social relations in organized sport programs not only sensitizes participants to the discipline of the larger society but also develops the types of social characteristics, self-images, and class identifications that are important factors for complacently fitting into adult roles. In effect, then, the social relationships typically found in organized youth sport—the relationships between coaches and athletes, athletes and athletes, and athletes and their sport tasks—replicate the hierarchical division of labor and the social values, in part through a correspondence between these internal social relationships and those of the larger society.

I am not suggesting that youth sport is some kind of ideological mirror of the dominant interests in present society; my argument is not a mechanistic vulgar Marxism that conceives of sport as simply a repository of dominant group beliefs and practices. I do contend, however, that a crucial first step in understanding cultural activities of any kind, sports included, is to situate them within their social and historical contexts (Gruneau, 1983; Hoberman, 1984; Morgan, 1985). The correspondence between sport and the social conditions in which we live is unmistakable, but I agree with Morgan (1985) that ''The social-historical backdrop of...sports, and the constitutive rules of which they are comprised, does not warrant tying them too closely to the rest of life'' (p. 63).

Does having disclaimed a strict determinist view but pointing out the inadequacies of naive idealism leave me with one foot in each of two boats sailing in opposite directions? I think not. I want to argue that professional leaders and interested citizens throughout the country need to become concerned about the directions that children's sport is taking. A first step in doing this is to develop an historical understanding of the cultural context and social practice from which the notion that sport builds character originated. In 19th-century England, where the idea that sport experiences developed particular social characteristics which then transferred to other social situations, there was an intelligible interrelatedness between social purpose, process, and outcome. Whether sport actually did what it was presumed to do is beside the point. In order for sport to have the potential to fulfill the expectations of it, purpose and process must be linked together. Social outcomes are a result of a particular pattern of social relationships. In other words, if a particular set of social traits is to be developed via a set of social experiences, there must be an affinity between the two. To believe otherwise is to engage in wishful thinking.

A second step is to make a critical analysis of current youth sport enterprises. I propose that sport can be employed in ways that differ from dominant group interests. I contend that the tendencies of current programs reflect dominant group interests primarily for lack of opposition to current practices. As a result, youth sport has taken on all of the trappings of the commodified sports industry. The social hegemony of commodification in youth sport is seen in its authoritarian and hierarchical organization, endorsement of the performance principle, meritocracy, overemphasis on winning, assault on records, and the increasing use of child athletes as public entertainers. Albinson (1976) aptly summed up the current situation by saying that to expect youth sport (he was referring to ice hockey) to encourage "personal growth, honor, generosity, tolerance, or just plain fun, may simply be to overlook the degree to which the logic of our adult world structures minor [sport]" (p. 390).

If there is a genuine, widespread public interest in really promoting youth sport as a medium for personal enrichment and development, enabling participants to practice and learn the social characteristics for which physical activity has been valorized, then public discussion and debate is called for.[2] Indeed, imminent critique (Adorno, 1981) of present practices is necessary. Where is this going on today? Where are the present assumptions about children's sport being challenged? There seems to be no critical commentary on present sport forms. Unfortunately, those who work in sports (physical educators, coaches, etc.) are some of the most uncritical. Where are the professional debates on this issue? Granted, a few members of the American Academy of Physical Education are making efforts to improve youth sport, but they are only a speck in the world of youth sport.

I close with this thought. The pressures to make youth sports little more than a reproduction of dominant group interests is powerful. If this tendency is to be challenged, then deliberate, well-planned, and executed action will have to take place. If it is not, I shall have to agree with Webb (1969) that "to continue the sophomoric and even moronic insistence on [sport's] contribution to the development of such 'sweetheart' characteristics as steadfastness, honor, generosity, courage, tolerance, [and other good character traits,] is to ignore its structural and value similarities" to the socioeconomic structure and the contributions that youth sport makes to participation in American society.

---

[2]There is a separate and important issue of whether sport should be deliberately used as an instrumental cultural activity, but this issue will not be addressed here.

REFERENCES

ADORNO, T.W. (1981). *Prisms.* Cambridge, MA: MIT Press.

ALBINSON, J.G. (1976). The "professional orientation" of the amateur hockey coach. In R.S. Gruneau & J.G. Albinson (Eds.), *Canadian sport: Sociological perspectives* (pp. 377-390). Don Mills, Ontario: Addison-Wesley.

BRUNER, J., Jolly, A., & Sylva, K. (Eds.). (1976). *Play: Its role in evolution and development.* New York: Penguin.

COAKLEY, J.G. (1984, July). *Mead's theory on the development of the self: Implications for organized youth sport programs.* Paper presented at the Olympic Scientific Congress on Sport, Sociology of Sport Session, Eugene, OR.

ERIKSON, E.H. (1963). *Childhood and society.* New York: Norton.

FREUD, S. (1959). *Beyond the pleasure principle.* New York: Bantam.

FREUD, S. (1963). *Jokes and their relation to the unconscious.* New York: Norton.

GRUNEAU, R.S. (1983). *Class, sports, and social development.* Amherst: University of Massachusetts Press.

HOBERMAN, J.M. (1984). *Sport and political ideology.* Austin: University of Texas Press.

KISTLER, J.W. (1957). Attitudes expressed about behavior demonstrated in certain specific situations. *Proceedings of the College Physical Education Association,* **60**, 55-58.

LOY, J.W., Birrell, S., & Rose, D. (1976). Attitudes held toward agonistic activities as a function of selected social identities. *Quest,* **26**, 81-93.

MALONEY, T., & Petrie, B. (1972). Professionalization of attitudes toward play among Canadian school pupils as a function of sex, grade, and athletic participation. *Journal of Leisure Research,* **4**, 184-195.

MANGAN, J.A. (1981). *Athleticism in the Victorian and Edwardian public school.* London: Cambridge University Press.

McINTOSH, P.C. (1957). Games and gymnastics for two nations in one. In J.G. Dixon, P.C. McIntosh, A.D. Munrow, & R.F. Willetts (Eds.), *Landmarks in the history of physical education* (pp. 177-208). London: Routledge & Kegal Paul.

MEAD, G.H. (1934). *Mind, self, and society.* Chicago: University of Chicago Press.

MORGAN, W.J. (1985). "Radical" social theory of sport: A conceptual emendation. *Sociology of Sport Journal,* **2**, 56-71.

PIAGET, J. (1962). *Play, dreams, and imitation in childhood.* New York: Norton.

PIAGET, J. (1965). *The moral judgment of the child.* New York: Free Press.

RICHARDSON, D. (1962). Ethical conduct in sport situations. *Proceedings of the National College Physical Education Association for Men,* **66**, 98-103.

ROBERTS, J., Arth, M.J., & Bush, R.R. (1959). Games in culture. *American Anthropologist,* **61**, 597-605.

SAGE, G.H. (1980). Orientations toward sport of male and female athletes. *Journal of Sport Psychology,* **2,** 355-362.

SCANLAN, T.K., & Lewthwaite, R. (1984). Social psychological aspects of competition for male youth sport participants: I. Predictors of competitive stress. *Journal of Sport Psychology,* **6,** 208-226.

SCANLAN, T.K., & Passer, M.W. (1978). Factors related to competitive stress among male youth sports participants. *Medicine and Science of Sports,* **10,** 103-108.

SCANLAN, T.K., & Passer, M.W. (1979). Sources of competitive stress in young female athletes. *Journal of Sport Psychology,* **1,** 151-159.

SUTTON-SMITH, B. (1974, Fall). Toward an anthropology of play. *The Association for the Anthropological Study of Play, Newsletter,* **1,** 1-10.

SUTTON-SMITH, B., & Roberts, J.M. (1970). The cross-cultural and psychological study of games. In G. Luschen (Ed.), *The cross-cultural analysis of sport and games* (pp. 100-108). Champaign, IL: Stipes.

WEBB, H. (1969). Professionalization of attitudes toward play among adolescents. In G.S. Kenyon (Ed.), *Aspects of Contemporary Sport Sociology* (pp. 161-178). Chicago: The Athletic Institute.

Physical Activity and Self-Esteem Development in Children: A Meta-Analysis

Joseph J. Gruber
University of Kentucky

Emotional development of children has long been a primary objective of physical education. Virtually every foundational text in our professional literature discusses the mental health value of play and physical activity. I have been asked to present information on the contributions of physical activity to children's psychological development. Completed research has focused primarily on elements of self-esteem.

Exploring self-esteem is a natural phenomena since pre- and postnatal experiences of the infant are bodily in nature. The body is the instrument of action and communication for developing infants and children. Thus a basic body concept emerges. This gradually evolves over time into a more global self-concept and self-esteem. Simply put, self-concept is our perception of self and self-esteem is the value we place on our self-image. Self-esteem is a basic element in a child's personality development and is believed to be a motivational springboard into future environmental experiences which, over time, shape elements of personality into more definable constructs.

Comments are restricted to studies involving preadolescent children, but with two exceptions: cross-sectional studies beginning with early elementary school age and extending into adolescence, and studies involving trainable mentally retarded individuals through 18 years of age. This review is also delimited to the literature of the past 20 years, generated by four independent computer searches. These searches provided titles and/or abstracts for 82 independent articles and 25 doctoral dissertations. Reading eliminated 23 as unsuitable to the topic of this paper. Most of the remaining 84 explored the relationship between physical activity and aspects of self-esteem in children.

METHODS

In analyzing the literature, we have adopted the traditional voting procedure and the meta-analysis approach advocated by Glass, McGaw, and Smith (1981). The articles generated by our search were reviewed and subdivided into five categories, and the voting procedure applied to those articles arrived at a consensus for philosophical or statistical significance. Category I included 10 "belief" articles, all 10 professing belief in the value of play. Category II included 17 clinical case studies or small-sample investigations with no data analyses—all 17 indicated that disturbed children show a reduction in inappropriate behaviors due in part to directed play or physical activity.

Category III included 27 controlled experimental studies having sufficient data to permit calculating an effect size. Eighteen of these studies declared findings that were statistically significant, while nine reported nonsignificant results. Category IV included 11 simple correlational or extreme group difference studies of which eight professed significance and three failed to achieve significance. Category V included 19 articles that, due to inadequate information or serious design flaws, do not meet the criteria for conducting an effective meta-analysis. In the overview, 53 of the 65 studies claimed that forces of play and physical activity contribute to development in the affective domain.

The voting procedure leaves much to be desired even though most of the studies in Category III were significant. We do not know if self-esteem is barely improved or greatly improved. Summing up levels of statistical significance reveals little about the strength or importance of a relationship.

Meta-analysis moves us away from using levels of statistical significance as an indicator of study value. In other words, meta-analysis through a synthesis of relevant independent studies attempts to answer the question, how significant are study findings in a more practical sense? To answer this question one must calculate an effect size for the conditions that are hypothesized to have an influence on the dependent variable. An effect size is calculated as follows: The mean of the control group is subtracted from the mean of the experimental group, and the difference is divided by the appropriate standard deviation value. To calculate the effect sizes in this paper, a pooled estimate of the standard deviation (weighted for sample size) was used. When means and standard deviations were provided in the study reports, these statistics were used to estimate each effect size (Hedges & Olkin, 1985). The resultant effect size is a value expressed in standard units on the baseline of the normal probability curve. The mean of the control group is the mean ordinate on the curve, with the experimental group mean deviating from this central value.

If we have calculated an effect size = .91 units above the mean, we see this includes 32% of the area under the curve. Hence, we can say that the average score of pupils in the experimental group exceeded the score attained by 82% of those in the control group. If all studies were conducted by investigators under exactly the same conditions, there would be no need for a meta-analysis because differences in study findings would be due to statistical error.

The real world of research is composed of different people exploring a similar variable (self-concept) under varying conditions in different environments. Results can fluctuate markedly from study to study. Here meta-analysis is most helpful since we can average effect sizes in studies having rather similar design characteristics, and in addition calculate a grand mean effect size for all studies. In order to calculate an effect size, a study must include sufficient data. Means, standard deviations, mean squares, probability levels, and *t* and *F*-ratios must be included for all main effect and interaction comparisons.

The literature in Category III was utilized for the meta-analysis. These research reports contained sufficient tabular information to permit calculation of main effect sizes using one of the estimation procedures described in Glass et al. (1981). Effect sizes were calculated for main effect comparisons that appeared to contribute information relative to the influence of directed play and/or physical education in enhancing elements of self-concept and other related personality dimensions in children. Effect sizes were not calculated for higher order interaction effects due to a large inequality of subjects across cells. In addition, most studies did not report accurate data relative to interaction error mean squares. All effect sizes were adjusted for the bias in estimating their relevant population values by multiplying each effect size by the appropriate correction factor (Glass et al., 1981; Hedges & Olkin, 1985).

Various characteristics of studies were coded into categories that were believed to influence the effects of physical activity on the dependent variable. These categories were subdivided into seven areas: subjects, design features, measuring instruments, length of study, teaching methods, curriculum, and publication status. Each coding category is composed of at least two characteristics. Related review articles and our professional judgment were used in establishing the code categories and deciding which characteristic within a category was present in each study. We coded studies on two separate occasions and only rarely were we unable to assign an appropriate characteristic to an effect size.

RESULTS AND DISCUSSION

Some studies explored the effects of play and physical activity using more than one program of activity under more than one condition. Hence, the number of effect sizes calculated exceeded the number of studies. Thus, 43 main effect sizes were calculated from the 27 studies reviewed. A summary of the characteristics and adjusted effect sizes for each study is presented in Table 1.

An overall average effect size of .41 ($s = .43$) was determined that amounted to slightly less than one-half of a standard deviation across all types of main effects. This finding suggests that participation in directed play and physical education programs influences the development of self-concept in children since the average score of children in the experimental groups will exceed the scores obtained by 66% of those in the control groups. However, the various coding categories are supposed to moderate this effect size. Thus, an effect size was calculated for each characteristic within a coding category. These effect sizes across categories appear in Figure 1 and permit us to make more meaningful comparisons. A statistical analysis of these differences among average effect sizes was not attempted because several of the categories are related and in some cases a small number of effect sizes determine the average effect.

Subjects

A rather large difference is noted in Figure 1 when comparing the average effect size of .34 from studies involving normal children with an effect size of .57 in those studies conducted on the handicapped. Children in the latter category represented the emotionally disturbed, trainable mentally retarded, economically disadvantaged, educable mentally retarded, and perceptually handicapped. Their mean effect size was well above the grand mean for all effect sizes. This appears to be an expected finding. For years the handicapped have lagged behind their age group in acquiring cognitive and motor skills, which probably has led to continual negative feedback. When placed into enrichment programs conducted by trained and understanding teachers who provide individual attention, the handicapped begin to feel important and experience success in activity programs. This leads to large improvement in their self-concept.

Table 1

Main Effect Sizes of Various Research Designs Investigating the Influence of Physical Activity on Self-Concept

Study	N/Sex	Subject characteristics	Curriculum	Method	Length of study	Dependent variable	Design features	Stat. sig.	Effect size
Lydon & Cheffers (1984)	285	Normal grades 1-5	Mvmt. expl. Gymnastics	Horizontal teach Vertical teach	1 semester 3 times/wk 45 min period	Mart.-Zaic. self-concept	2 exper. 1 control Complex ANCOVA	No	.07 .13
Roswal, Frith, & Dunleavy (1984)	32 / 16M 16F	EMR M-age 9.7 F-age 10.8	Mvmt. motor development	Clinical instructor	9 wks, 2 hrs ea. Saturday	Mart.-Zaic. self-concept	1 exper. 1 control Simple ANCOVA	Yes	1.51
Schempp, Cheffers, & Zaichkowsky (1983)	208	Normal elementary grades 1-5	Mvmt. educ. Gymnastics	Shared decision Teacher dominated control No phys ed	8 wks 1-45 min ea. wk	Mart.-Zaic. self-concept	2 exper. 1 control Random Complex ANOVA	Yes[+] (2 exper)	.59
Smith (1983)*	53 / 34F 19M	Normal grades 4, 5	Aerobic (run) Yoga Control (P.E.)	Traditional	3 times/wk 9 wks	Piers-Harris self-concept	2 exper. 1 control Complex ANCOVA	No	.37 .17

(continued)

Table 1 (cont.)

Study	N/Sex	Subject characteristics	Curriculum	Method	Length of study	Dependent variable	Design features	Stat. sig.	Effect size
Percy (1981)	30	Normal grades 5, 6	Running	N/A	3 times/wk 7 wks	Coopersmith self-concept	1 exper. 1 control Simple Random	Yes	1.14
Lynch (1980)*	101	Normal kindergarten age 4, 5, 6	Mvmt. motor development	Horizontal teach Vertical teach	1 period/wk 30 min 9 periods	Mart.-Zaic. self-concept	4 exper. 2 control Complex ANCOVA	No+	−.00 −.00
Platzer (1976)	26	Normal age 4, 5	Perc. motor	N/A	30 min daily 5 days/wk 10/wks	Goodenough, draw tree, house person (self-esteem)	Exper. Control Random Simple	Yes	.80
Puretz (1975)*	150F	Disadvantaged elementary	Modern dance	N/A	4 mos 1/2 hr daily	Lippsitt self-concept	Exper. Control Simple Equated	Yes Yes	.43 .35
Lamport (1974)*	102	Learning disabilities age 7-9	Perc. motor	N/A	4 mos	Thomas self-concept	Pre-post Complex ANCOVA	No No No	.09 .23 .13

(continued)

Table 1 (cont.)

Study	N / Sex	Subject characteristics	Curriculum	Method	Length of study	Dependent variable	Design features	Stat. sig.	Effect size
Smith (1982)	66	Normal grade 3	Elem. P.E. Mvmt. explor. Perc.-motor	Traditional	twice/wk 8 wks	Mart.-Zaic. self-concept	2 exper. 1 control Matched, Random Complex	No	.16 .08
Simpson & Meaney (1979)	20	TMR I.Q. 40-60	Ski instruction	N/A	1 3/4 hrs/wk 5 wks	Lippsitt self-concept	Exper. Control Gain scores Simple	Yes	.92
Martinek & Johnson (1979)	100 52M 48F	Normal grades 4, 5	Soccer Gymnastics Fitness	Expectancy High group Low group	30 min/wk 16 wks	Mart.-Zaic. self-concept	Extreme Groups Complex ANCOVA	Yes[+]	.98
Culhane (1979)*	57M	Emot. dist. MR age 9-16	Aerobics, Swim, Run, Full run, Mild run	N/A	Gym 3 times/wk 10 wks	Piers-Harris self-concept	5 treat groups *Adj. pre-post* Extreme Conditioned High-low	Yes	.30 2.27

(continued)

Table 1 (cont.)

Study	N/Sex	Subject characteristics	Curriculum	Method	Length of study	Dependent variable	Design features	Stat. sig.	Effect size
Martinek, Cheffers, & Zaichkowsky (1978)	344	Normal grades 1-5	Motor skill development Perc.-motor Gymnastics	Traditional	45 min/wk 10 wks	Mart.-Zaic. self-concept	Exper. Control Complex ANCOVA	Yes	.28
Smith, Smoll, & Curtis (1979)	31 coaches 187 players	Baseball players age 9-12	Little League baseball	Coaches effectiveness training	2 hrs, 2 wks feedback observe 10 games	Coopersmith self-esteem of players	Exper. Control Pre-post Simple	Yes / No	.27 / .27
Koocher, (1971)	65M	Normal age 7-15	Aquatics Summer camp, learn to swim	N/A	2 wks	Ideal self - Self discrepancy	2 exper. 1 control Matched Simple	Yes / Yes	.68 / .85
Yeatts & Gordon (1968)	75 / 38M 37F	Normal Prior 3 yrs experience to grade 7	Elementary phys ed	Teach-specialist No P.E. teacher	Prior 3 yrs	Gordon self-concept	Specialist No special- ist, Extre- gps., Poor	No	.16
McGowan, Jarman, & Pedersen (1974)	37M	Grade 7 age 12-13	Vigorous P.E. Running Team Games	N/A	18 wks	Tennessee self-concept	Exper. Control Random Corr. "t" Simple	Yes	.56

(continued)

Table 1 (cont.)

Study	N / Sex	Subject characteristics	Curriculum	Method	Length of study	Dependent variable	Design features	Stat. sig.	Effect size
Martinek (1978)	99 46M 53F	Normal grade 3, 4	Mvmt. educ.	Teach-decision Share-decision	twice/wk 10 wks 40 min per	Body concept	Exper. Control Complex ANCOVA	No Yes No[+]	.21 .42 .19
Chasey, Swartz, & Chasey (1978)*	44	TMR I.Q. 40 Age 14.6	Fitness Runs Gymnastics Movement	N/A	5 wks 1 hr/day	Body image	Exper. Control Pre-post Simple	Yes	.60
Martinek, Zaichkowsky, & Cheffers (1977)	345	Normal grade 1-5	Elementary phys ed Mvmt. motor development	Vertical Horizontal methods	45 min twice/wk 10 wks	Mart.-Zaic. self-concept	2 exper. Control Complex Good control ANCOVA	Yes	.24 .48
Mauser & Reynolds (1977)	12 2F 10M	Perc. deficits age 4-12	Perceptual-motor	N/A	8 wks	Mart.-Zaic. self-concept	Pre-post t-correlation	No	.34
Nahme-Huang, et al. (1977)	36	EMR hospitalized	Perceptual-motor, Clown workshop	N/A	45 min/wk 6 wks	Body image Behav. rating	2 exper. Control Poor	No Yes	-.06 .32

(continued)

Table 1 (cont.)

Study	N/Sex	Subject characteristics	Curriculum	Method	Length of study	Dependent variable	Design features	Stat. sig.	Effect size
Bruya, (1977)	72 / 36M 36F	Normal grade 4	Basketball skills	Traditional	30 min twice/wk 4 wks	Piers-Harris self-concept	2 exper. 2 control Complex ANCOVA	No	.10
Schneider* (1977)	301 / 156M 145F	Normal grade 7	Phys. educ. Mvmt. educ. Mime	Traditional	twice/wk 7 1/2 wks	Body image self-concept	2 exper. 2 control Complex ANCOVA	No[+]	.17 .03
Duke, Johnson, & Nowicki (1977)	109 / 74M 35F	Normal age 6-14	Sport camp Fitness	N/A	3 1/2 hrs daily 5 wks	Nowicki-Strickland locus of control	Pre-post ANCOVA Fair	Yes Yes	.35 .36
Hawkins & Gruber (1982)	94M	Normal age 9-12	Baseball	N/A	3 times/wk 3 1/2 mos	Coopersmith gen. self	Pre-post Diff. scores No control	Yes	.24

*Unpublished study

[+] Additional significant interaction effects.

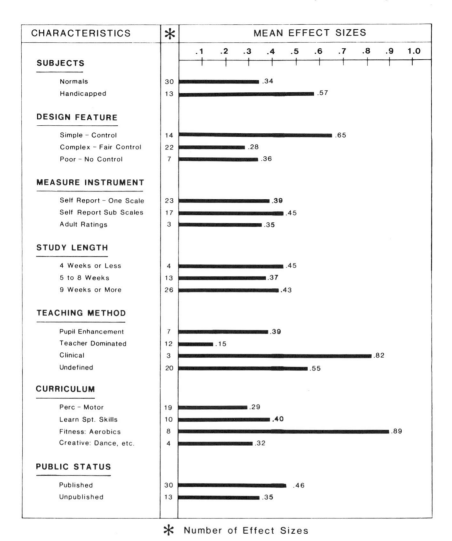

☀ Number of Effect Sizes

Figure 1—Mean main effect sizes among various coding characteristics.

Martinek and Karper (1982) found that entry level self-concepts of nonhandicapped pupils in physical education classes were significantly higher than the self-concepts of handicapped pupils in the same classes in the elementary grades. It is rather obvious that the greatest gain is seen in those who need it most. And it is noteworthy that normal children also experienced a slight improvement in self-esteem, given that findings on normal adults relative to significant changes in self-esteem following chronic exercise are somewhat inconclusive (Morgan, Roberts, Brand, & Feinerman, 1970; Morgan, 1982, 1985).

Design Features

The data in Figure 1 clearly show the superiority of a simple, well-controlled study in determining effects of physical activity on children's self-concept. The average effect size of .65 was almost twice the effect size of complex designs. The more simple design was characterized by one experimental and one control group, subjects assigned at random to groups and groups randomly assigned to treatment conditions. Only one dependent variable was involved. Treatment conditions were carefully defined: teachers trained in the method, and a control group that received no organized physical activity with a teacher was indicated. The other designs usually were complex factorials with three or four independent and dependent variables. Intact classes were assigned to treatment conditions. In some cases the control groups received regular physical education. Some attempts at statistical control with covariance designs were noted. At best, fair control characterized these designs. Other complex designs either had no control group or attempts at control were quite poor. Feltz and Landers (1983) also found that simple control designs had slightly larger effect sizes when compared with other designs investigating mental practice effects on motor skill learning.

Measuring Instrument

The average effect sizes for the three types of measuring instruments determined from the various reports were all rather similar and very close to the grand mean of .41. Our notion that a short measuring instrument producing one scale score would be more effective than a device having a variety of subscale scores was not tenable. In addition, the effect sizes of adults' and children's ratings of self-concept were similar.

Study Length

The data in Figure 1 show that the duration of the studies was unrelated to their average effect sizes. The three average effect sizes were all around the grand mean of .41. It is tempting to say that the beneficial effects of physical activity on enhancing self-concept will occur in the first weeks of an activity program. This may or may not be the case. We would recommend that future researchers use time series designs and keep track of time on task and ratio of positive to negative reinforcement for each child. Changes in psychological variables over the time that children are involved in activity could then be plotted. Follow-up measures should also be taken for several years following the experiment so as to determine retention effects.

Teaching Methods

A rather large effect size of .82 for clinical methods is noted in Figure 1. Pupils were either institutionalized or placed into special perceptual-motor clinics in addition to their regular classes. These children benefited from carefully planned programs conducted by specially trained teachers. One also notes in Figure 1 that the pupil enhancement method is slightly better than the traditional teacher dominated style. Our description of pupil enhancement applies to those teaching methods whereby teachers and children interact in the process of decision-making. One cannot help but feel important when consulted by a significant authority figure about class activities.

It is important to note that the effect size of .39 was obtained when the pupil enhancement method was compared with either the teacher dominated method or a control group whereby the teacher utilized a traditional approach. We also observe in Figure 1 that a large number of effect sizes were averaged for an undefined method effect size of .55. Those study reports did not specify a method in detail because it was not the purpose of the study to investigate the influence of instructional methodology on self-concept. It is likely that these investigations represented a variety of teaching methods.

Curriculum

The influence of curriculum is of interest to all elementary physical education specialists. It is evident from the data in Figure 1 that all four of the curricula contribute to self-concept development in children. Physical fitness and aerobic activities are clearly superior, with a mean effect size of .89, well above the grand mean of .41. The immediate feedback one gets from meeting daily fitness goals in activities that do not require complex motor skills may partially explain the large effect size. The pupil readily detects improvement and may have a feeling of body mastery as he or she successfully meets the demands of fitness activities. Perceptual-motor or motor development programs, programs designed to teach sports skills (gymnastics, soccer, skiing, basketball), and programs of dance, mime, or other creative movement all seem to have similar effects and approach the grand mean.

Publication Status

There does not appear to be a large mean effect size difference between articles that are published or unpublished, although the published literature has a slight lead. Feltz and Landers (1983), on the other hand, found large-effect size differences favoring published articles.

A number of experimental articles reported other main and interaction effects, the majority not lending themselves to the calculation of an effect size. However, we will report on the findings in an effort to shed some light on trends. There is no concensus for a gender difference in self-concept improvement. Significant differences in improvement were reported favoring 7th-grade boys (Schneider, 1972), two studies favored girls (Martinek, 1978; Schempp, Cheffers, & Zaichkowsky, 1983), and no gender differences were reported in four investigations (Bruya, 1977; Martinek, Zaichkowsky, & Cheffers, 1977; Schneider, 1977; Smith, 1982).

Younger children appear to profit more from shared decision teaching styles when compared with traditional teaching methods (Lynch, 1980; Martinek, 1978; Schempp et al., 1983). Martinek, Cheffers, and Zaichkowsky (1978) also found that 1st- and 2nd-grade children improved in self-concept more than did older children. Hawkins and Gruber (1982) did not find any differences in self-esteem scores in 9-, 10-, 11-, and 12-year-old boys exposed to a season of baseball. In addition, no racial differences in self-concept improvement were detected (Martinek et al., 1978; Smith, 1982). Future research must explore age, sex, race, and possible socioeconomic factors as mediating variables. Very few attempts were made to control for these variables in the literature reviewed for this paper. Problems with research designs involving self-esteem have been well reviewed by Sonstroem (1981).

Based on the findings of the meta-analysis conducted under conditions specified in this paper, we may conclude that participation in directed play and/or physical education programs contributes to the development of self-esteem in elementary school-age children. It is not clear why physical activity is related to improvement in self-esteem. Morgan (1985) suggests either a distraction, an endorphin, or monamine (brain neurotransmitter) hypothesis in mediating improvement in affective states. It may be that these three factors act in a synergistic manner.

The neurotransmitter hypothesis has not been explored in children but equivocal work on animals and adult humans has been reported (Morgan, 1985). The distractability hypothesis claims that individuals improve in the exercise mode simply because they are temporarily freed from the routine stress and stimuli of environments that differ from the physical education class. We offer some argument against this hypothesis by contrasting vigorous (aerobic fitness) exercise with other types of less vigorous activity and Hawthorne control groups viewed as relevant distractors.

The data in Figure 1 show an effect size of .89 for aerobic activities, .40 for sports instruction, .29 for perceptual-motor, and .32 for dance. Culhane (1979) found the greatest improvements in self-concept statements and teachers' and parents' behavior ratings for the highest conditioned (O_2 uptake) children when compared with the least conditioned group. Smith (1983) compared aerobics, yoga (Hawthorne), and a regular physical education nonaerobic control group. Effect sizes of .37 and .17 were calculated for the aerobic and yoga groups, respectively. Chasey, Swartz, and Chasey (1978) compared a fitness (aerobics, runs, gymnastics) program with a Hawthorne quiet recreation group (quiet games, painting, songs, walking) and another control group that received no physical education or recreation. They found significant differences in body image improvement between the fitness and control groups (effect size = .60), and no differences between the two control groups.

One can conclude that affective domain objectives are quite valid when developing physical education programs for children. The data in this paper clearly demonstrate the superiority of physical fitness activities in developing self-esteem when compared with other components of the elementary physical education curriculum.

The implication of this finding is quite clear, especially for those children who feel insecure and in time could develop behavior problems. Noland and Gruber (1978) have shown that emotionally disturbed children with low levels of self-esteem tend to be introverted and have high trait-anxiety scores. Positive competency attitudes are developed through proper physical education experiences. This attitude is quite important because what one thinks of him/herself may be the prime determiner of future behavior.

REFERENCES

ABRAMSON, R.M., Hoffman, L., & Johns, C.A. (1979). Play group psychotherapy for early latency-age children on an inpatient psychiatric unit. *International Journal of Group Psychotherapy, 29*(3), 383-392.

ALDER, H. (1982). Children with problems in physical education in school II: Physical factors and psychosocial problems. *Acta Paedopsychiatrica,* **48**(1), 33-46.

ANDERSON, E.G. (1978). The child in hospital: Play and emotional needs. *Australian Nurses Journal,* **7**(11), 54-57.

[1]ANDERSON, J.R. (1974). The effects of structured physical interactions in psychotherapy on anxiety and specific behavioral variables in children. (Doctoral dissertation, Boston University School of Education.) *DAI,* **35**(6-A), 3416-3417.

AUXTER, D.M., Zahar, E., & Ferrini, L. (1967). Body image development of emotionally disturbed children. *American Corrective Therapy Journal,* **21**(5), 154-155.

BACHMAN, J.E., & Fuqua, R.W. (1983). Management of inappropriate behaviors of trainable mentally impaired students using antecedent exercise. *Journal of Applied Behavior Analysis,* **16**(4), 477-484.

BARTON, J. (1982). Aerobic dance and the mentally retarded—A winning combination. *Physical Educator,* **39**(1), 25-29.

BEISER, H.R. (1979). Formal games in diagnosis and therapy. *Journal of the American Academy of Child Psychiatry,* **18**(3), 480-491.

BILLINGTON, G.F. (1972). Play program reduces children's anxiety, speeds recoveries. *Modern Hospital,* **118**(4), 90-92.

BROWN, R.S. (1982). Exercise and mental health in the pediatric population. *Clinic Sports Medicine,* **1**(3), 515-527.

BRUYA, L.D. (1977). Effect of selected movement skills on positive self-concept. *Perceptual and Motor Skills,* **45**(1), 252-254.

CHASEY, W.C., Swartz, J.D., & Chasey, C.G. (1978). Effect of motor development on body image scores for institutionalized mentally retarded children. *American Journal of Mental Deficiency,* **78**(4), 440-445.

CLIFFORD, E., & Clifford, M. (1967). Self-concepts before and after survival training. *British Journal of Social and Clinical Psychology,* **6**(4), 241-248.

CULHANE, J.C. (1979). Physical fitness and self-concept: An investigation of self-concept modification by aerobic conditioning. (Doctoral dissertation, George Washington University.) *DAI,* **40**(4-B), 1884-1885.

DUKE, M., Johnson, T.C., & Nowicki, S. (1977). Effects of sports fitness camp experience on locus of control orientation in children 6-14. *Research Quarterly,* **48**(2), 280-283.

EARLS, N. (1973). *Final evaluation report for Project Hope.* (Bureau No. BR-077-1-70-033). Washington, DC: Bureau of Elementary and Secondary Education (DHEW/DE). (ERIC Document Reproduction Service No. ED 102 127.)

FELKER, D.W. (1968). Relationship between self-concept, body build, and perception of father's interest in sports in boys. *Research Quarterly,* **39**(3), 513-517.

---

[1]Microfiche of all dissertations were obtained for review.

FELKER, D.W., & Kay, R.S. (1971). Self-concept, sports interests, sports participation, and body type of seventh and eighth grade boys. *Journal of Psychology,* **78**(2), 223-228.

FELTZ, D.L., & Landers, D.M. (1983). The effects of mental practice on motor skill learning and performance: A meta-analysis. *Journal of Sport Psychology,* **5**(1), 25-57.

FRETZ, B.R., & Johnson, W.R. (1973). Behavioral changes in children participating in a physical developmental clinic. *Perceptual and Motor Skills,* **36**(3), 855-862.

GLASS, G.V., McGaw, B., & Smith, M.L. (1981). *Meta-analysis in social research.* Beverly Hills, CA: Sage Publications.

GUYOT, G.W., Fairchild, L., & Hill, M. (1981). Physical fitness, sport participation, body build, and self-concept of elementary school children. *International Journal of Sport Psychology,* **12**(2), 105-116.

HAWKINS, D.B., & Gruber, J.J. (1982). Little League baseball and players' self-esteem. *Perceptual and Motor Skills,* **55**, 1335-1340.

HEDGES, L.V., & Olkin, I. (1985). Statistical methods for meta-analysis. New York: Academic Press.

HUSSEIN, H.H. (1980). The effects of a structured physical activity program on the physical fitness and self-esteem of trainable mentally retarded (TMR) individuals. (Doctoral dissertation, Middle Tennessee State University.) *DAI,* **41**(5-A). 2006.

HYDE, N.D. (1971). Play therapy: The troubled child's self-encounter. *American Journal of Nursing,* **71**(7), 1366-1370.

JOHNSON, W.R., Fretz, B.R., & Johnson, J.A. (1968). Changes in self-concepts during a physical development program. *Research Quarterly,* **39**(3), 560-565.

KAHN, L.E. (1982). Self-concept and physical fitness of retarded students as correlates of social interaction between retarded and nonretarded students. (Doctoral dissertation, New York University.) *DAI,* **45**(7-A), 2275.

KARPER, W.B., & Martinek, J.G. (1982). Differential influences of various instructional factors on self-concepts of handicapped and non-handicapped children in mainstreamed physical education classes. *Perceptual and Motor Skills,* **54**(3), 831-835.

KARPER, W.B., & Martinek, J.G. (1983). Motor performance and self-concept of handicapped and non-handicapped children in integrated physical education classes. *American Corrective Therapy Journal,* **37**(3), 91-95.

KAY, R.S., Felker, D.W., & Varoz, R.O. (1972). Sports interests and abilities as contributors to self-concept in junior high school boys. *Research Quarterly,* **43**(2), 208-215.

KEITH, C.A. (1972). The effect of swimming upon self-concept and selected motor fitness components in educable mentally retarded children. (Doctoral dissertation, University of Southern Mississippi.) *DAI,* **33**(9-A), 4917.

KERN, L., Koegel, R.L., Dyer, K., Blew, P.A., & Fenton, L.R. (1982). The effects of physical exercise on self-stimulation and appropriate responding in autistic children. *Journal of Autism Developmental Disorders,* **12**(4), 399-419.

KING, B.R. (1982). The influence of motor ability, self-concept, peer relationships, and reported interests on children's choices in physical education. (Doctoral dissertation, Boston University School of Education.) *DAI,* **43**(4-A), 1079.

KING, P.D., & Ekstein, R. (1967). The search for ego controls: Progression of play activity in psychotherapy with a schizophrenic child. *Psychoanalytic Review,* **54**(4), 639-648.

KLUGE, K.J. (1971). Behavioral changes in depressed pupils in the course of a play-therapeutic procedure. *Acta Paedopsychiatrica,* **38**(7), 221-227.

KOOCHER, G.P. (1971). Swimming, competence, and personality change. *Journal of Personality and Social Psychology,* **18**(3), 275-278.

LAMPORT, L.C. (1974). The effects of a specific perceptual-motor physical education program on the self-concept of children with learning disabilities. (Doctoral dissertation, University of New Mexico.) *DAI,* **36**(3-A), 1436-1437.

LEAL, M.R. (1966). Group analytic play therapy with preadolescent girls. *International Journal of Group Psychotherapy,* **16**(1), 58-61.

LOOVIS, E.M. (1978). Effects of participation in sport/physical education on the development of the exceptional child. *American Corrective Therapy Journal,* **32**(6), 167-169.

LOVASDAL, S. (1976). A multiple therapy approach in work with children. *International Journal of Group Psychotherapy,* **26**(4), 475-486.

LUDWIG, D.J., & Maeher, M.L. (1967). Changes in self-concept and stated behavioral preferences. *Child Development,* **38**(2), 453-467.

LUEBKE, L.L. (1977). A comparison of the effects of two programs of elementary physical education on the self-concept, knowledge of physical activity, and physical fitness of third grade children. (Doctoral dissertation, Marquette University.) *DAI,* **38**(10-A), 5992.

LYDON, M.C., & Cheffers, J.T.F. (1984). Decision making in elementary school age children: Effects on motor learning and self-concept development. *Research Quarterly for Exercise and Sport,* **55**(2), 135-140.

LYNCH, P.M. (1980). Effects of horizontal and vertical models of teaching on the development of motor ability, self-concept, and involvement levels of kindergarten children with regard to movement education. (Doctoral dissertation, Boston University School of Education.) *DAI,* **41**(5-A), 2069.

MAGILL, R.A., & Ash, M.J. (1979). Academic, psycho-social, and motor characteristics of participants and non-participants in children's sports. *Research Quarterly,* **50**(2), 230-240.

MANN, L., & Hilsendager, D.W. (1968a). Physical recreation: An old-new dimension in helping the emotionally disturbed child. *American Corrective Therapy Journal,* **22**(4), 131-135.

MANN, L., & Hilsendager, D.W. (1968b). The four phases: A new conceptual approach to physical education for emotionally disturbed children. *American Corrective Therapy Journal,* **22**(2), 43-45.

MARTINEK, T.J. (1978). Decision sharing in elementary school children: Effects on body concept and anxiety. *Perceptual and Motor Skills, 47*(3, pt. 1), 1015-1021.

MARTINEK, T.J., Cheffers, T.J., & Zaichkowsky, L.D. (1978). Physical activity, motor development and self-concept: Race and age differences. *Perceptual and Motor Skills, 46*(1), 147-154.

MARTINEK, T.J., & Johnson, S.B. (1979). Teacher expectations: Effect on dyadic interactions and self-concept in elementary age children. *Research Quarterly, 50*(1), 60-70.

MARTINEK, T.J., & Karper, W.B. (1982). Entry level motor performance and self-concepts of handicapped and non-handicapped children in mainstreamed physical education classes: A preliminary study. *Perceptual and Motor Skills, 55*(3, pt. 1), 1002.

MARTINEK, T.J., Zaichkowsky, L.D., & Cheffers, J.T. (1977). Decision making in elementary age children: Effects on motor skills and self-concept. *Research Quarterly, 48*(2), 349-357.

MAUL, T., & Thomas, J.R. (1975). Self-concept and participation in children's gymnastics. *Perceptual and Motor Skills, 41*(3), 701-702.

MAUSER, H.J., & Reynolds, R.P. (1977). Effects of a developmental physical activity program on children's body coordination and self-concept. *Perceptual and Motor Skills, 44*(3), 1057-1058.

MAYO, F.M. (1975). The effects of aerobics conditioning exercise on selected personality characteristics of seventh and eighth grade girls. *DAI, 35,* 4163-A.

McELROY, M. (1982). Consequences of perceived parental pressure on the self-esteem of youth sports participation. *American Corrective Therapy Journal, 36*(6), 164-167.

McGLENN, R.L. (1976). Relationship of personality and self-image change of high and low fitness adolescent males to selected activity programs. (Doctoral dissertation, United States International University.) *DAI, 37*(3-B), 1410-1411.

McGOWAN, R.W., Jarman, B.O., & Pedersen, D.M. (1974). Effects of a competitive endurance training program on self-concept and peer approval. *The Journal of Psychology, 86,* 57-60.

MORGAN, W.P. (1982). Psychological effects of exercise. *Behavior Medicine Update, 4,* 25-30.

MORGAN, W.P. (1985). Affective beneficence of vigorous physical activity. *Medicine and Science in Sports and Exercise, 17*(1), 94-100.

MORGAN, W.P., Roberts, J.A., Brand, F.R., & Feinerman, A.D. (1970). Psychological effect of chronic physical activity. *Medicine and Science in Sports, 2,* 213-217.

NAHME, H.L., Singer, D.G., Singer, J.L., & Wheaton, A.B. (1977). Imaginative play training and perceptual motor interventions with emotionally disturbed hospitalized children. *American Journal of Orthopsychiatry, 47*(2), 238-249.

NOLAND, M., & Gruber, J.J. (1978). Self-perception, personality, and behavior in emotionally disturbed children. *Behavioral Disorders, 4*(1), 6-12.

PERCY, L.E., Dziuban, C.D., & Martin, J.B. (1981). Analysis of effects of distance running on self-concepts of elementary students. *Perceptual and Motor Skills, 52*(1), 45.

PLATZER, W.S. (1976). Effect of perceptual motor training on gross-motor skill and self-concept of young children. *American Journal of Occupational Therapy,* **30**(7), 422-428.

PURETZ, S.L. (1975). *A comparison of the effects of dance and physical education on the self-concept of selected disadvantaged girls.* (ERIC Document Reproduction Service No. ED 103 405.)

RICHARDSON, P.A., Weinberg, R.S., Bruya, L., Baun, W., Jackson, A., Caton, J., & Bruya, L. (1980). Physical and psychological characteristics of young children in sports: A descriptive profile. *Physical Educator,* **37**(4), 187-191.

ROBERTS, A. (1978). Extraversion and outdoor play in middle childhood. *Educational Research,* **21**(1), 37-42.

ROSWAL, G., & Frith, G.H. (1980). The children's developmental play program: Physical activity designed to facilitate the growth and development of mildly handicapped children. *Education and Training of the Mentally Retarded,* **15**(4), 322-324.

ROSWAL, G., Frith, G., & Dunleavy, A. (1984). The effect of a developmental play program on the self-concept, risk taking behaviors, and motoric proficiency of mildly handicapped children. *Physical Educator,* **41**(1), 43-50.

RUPNOW, A.A. (1972). Anxiety and motor performance in children. (Doctoral dissertation, University of Utah.) *DAI,* **33**(6-A), 2752-2753.

RYAN, J.A. (1978). A study to determine the effects of body movement exercises on the body percept and body boundaries of young children. (Doctoral dissertation, University of Detroit.) *DAI,* **40**(7-B), 3421.

SCHEMPP, P.G., Cheffers, J.T.F., & Zaichkowsky, L.D. (1983). Influence of decision making on attitudes, creativity, motor skills, and self-concept in elementary children. *Research Quarterly for Exercise and Sport,* **54**(2), 183-189.

SCHNEIDER, F.J. (1977). The effect of movement exploration and mime on body image, self-concept, and body coordination of seventh grade children. (Doctoral dissertation, Boston University School of Education.) *DAI,* **38**(9-A), 5335-5336.

SEAMAN, J.A. (1972). The effects of a bowling program upon bowling skill, number concepts, and self-esteem of mentally retarded children. (Doctoral dissertation, Indiana University.) *DAI,* **33**(7-A), 3359-3360.

SIMPSON, H.M., & Meaney, C. (1979). Effects of learning to ski on self-concepts of mentally retarded children. *American Journal of Mental Deficiency,* **84**(1), 25-29.

SMILKSTEIN, G. (1980). Psychological trauma in children and youth in competitive sports. *Journal of Family Practice,* **10**(4), 737-739.

SMITH, L.F. (1977). An experiment with play therapy. *American Journal of Nursing,* **77**(12), 1963-1965.

SMITH, M.C. (1972). Reversing reversals. *Education and Training of the Mentally Retarded,* **7**(2), 91-93.

SMITH, R.E., Smoll, F.L., & Curtis, B. (1979). Coach effectiveness training: A cognitive-behavioral approach to enhancing relationship skills in youth sport coaches. *Journal of Sport Psychology,* **1**(1), 59-75.

SMITH, T. (1983). Competition trait anxiety in youth sport: Differences according to age, sex, race, and playing status. *Perceptual and Motor Skills, 57*(3), 1235-1238.

SMITH, T.L. (1982). Self-concepts and movement skills of third grade children after physical education programs. *Perceptual and Motor Skills, 54*(3, pt. 2), 1145-1146.

SMITH, T.P. (1983). An evaluation of the psychological effects of physical exercise on children. (Doctoral dissertation, DePaul University.) *DAI, 44*(7-B), 2260.

SONSTROEM, R.J. (1981). Exercise and self-esteem: Recommendations for expository research. *Quest, 33*(2), 124-139.

STANIFORD, D.J. (1983). Personalized physical education: Inviting success and the development of self-concept through movement. *Physical Educator, 40*(3), 154-158.

STEWART, M.A. (1971). Urinary nonadrenaline and playroom behavior in hyperactive children. *Lancet, 1*(1), 140.

TEAGARDIN, S.S. (1983). A study of self-concept in relation to physical fitness and motor abilities among elementary, middle, and high school girls. (Doctoral dissertation, East Texas State University.) *DAI, 44*(6-A), 1726.

TYLER, J.A. (1972). The relationship between self-concept and motor performance of second grade children. (Doctoral dissertation, Ohio State University.) *DAI, 33*(8-A), 4163.

ULTEA, C.A., Griffioen, D., & Schellekens, J. (1982). The reduction of anxiety in children: A comparison of the effects of systematic desensitization in vitro and systematic desensitization in vivo. *Behavioral Research and Therapy, 20*(1), 61-67.

WUNDHEILER, L.N. (1976). "Liberty Boy." The play of a schizophrenic child. *Journal of the American Academy of Child Psychiatry, 15*(3), 475-490.

YEATTS, P.P., & Gordon, I.J. (1968). Effects of physical education taught by a specialist on physical fitness and self-image. *Research Quarterly, 39*(3), 766-770.

Effects of Physical Activity on Intellectual Development and Academic Performance

Don R. Kirkendall
Kansas State University

> For in everything that men do the body is useful, and in all uses of the body it is of great importance to be in as high a state of physical efficiency as possible. Why, even in the process of thinking, in which the use of the body seems to be reduced to a minimum, it is a matter of common knowledge that grave mistakes may often be traced to bad health....But a sound and healthy body is a strong protection to a man. (cited in Van Dalen & Bennett, 1971, p. 61)

Who made this statement? Is this a recent declaration by one of our learned colleagues in the field of physical education? It so happens that Socrates made this observation in about 400 B.C. The tenet that the function and development of the mind is influenced by the health and care of the body is not a new idea or belief. Physical educators and many others have always believed that the development of a sound body will enhance the development of the mind. We need only look at the traditional general goals or objectives of physical education to see this.

Virtually all such objectives include the development of the child's intellect as one of the primary goals of physical education. While it might appear to be true that development of the mind is enhanced by proper physical activity, we would do well to assess the evidence supporting this unquestioned claim. That is the purpose of this article.

The concept of integrated development, drawing attention to the interrelationship between nonintellectual (especially motor, emotional, and social) and intellectual aspects, forms the basis for several theories of child development. One of the classical theories is the "organismic age" theory proposed by Olson (1949), who directed attention toward the interrelatedness of various phases of growth such as achievement in school, height and weight, dental and carpal growth, grip strength, and mental age. He converted each measure into a comparable age category and, after averaging all age scores, derived an overall score which was called organismic age.

The Gestalt psychologists have influenced other psychologists as well as educators by emphasizing that an individual functions as a whole within the environment and thus must be treated accordingly. Hall and Lindsey (1957) expressed the feelings of the Gestaltists very well when they said,

> The organism always behaves as a unified whole and not as a series of differential parts. Mind and body are not separate entities, nor does the mind consist of independent facul-

> ties or elements and the body of independent organs and processes. The organism is
> a single unity. What happens in a part affects the whole. (Hall & Lindsey, 1957, p. 297)

Another theory, the perceptual-motor concept of Kephart (1960), emphasizes the complete perceptual-motor development of a child. Kephart felt that the learning difficulties some children have may be partially explained by a perceptual-motor breakdown, since all behavior is basically motor behavior.

A similar theory proposed by Delacato (1959, 1963) emphasized the need for neurological organization which, in normal children, is the result of uninterrupted ontogenetic development. Therefore he advocated that if neural patterns are omitted during the child's neurological development, they could be introduced later in order to compensate for these missing links.

Neurologists recognize that in order for the organism to perceive a complex motor task correctly, all structures in the central nervous system must be fully developed and physiologically ready to integrate stimulus and response patterns. Hence, almost all theories are built on the basic assumption that perceptual-motor training which takes advantage of the relationship between sensory processes and motor responses acts through the cortex and lower brain centers to improve perceptual and motor functions. The rationale is that motor performance stimulates the central nervous system to such an extent that underdeveloped, dead, or dying cells will either be rehabilitated or their function assumed by other or newly generated cells.

Finally, Steinhaus (1964) called attention to the fact that the most important sense organ in the body is muscle tissue, since some 40% of the axons in the motor-nerve to a muscle are actually sensory fibers that carry impulses to the brain. Thus, the muscles that make up over half of our body weight are really the source of neural information, since they transmit information from the outside world to the central nervous system in different forms such as memory, concept formation, thinking, and reasoning.

The development and discussion of theory is an essential aspect in the growth of any field of study. However, theories cannot stand indefinitely on conjecture alone. Eventually they must be supported or refuted by scientific evidence, and this is where the going gets tough.

RESEARCH FINDINGS

In reviewing the literature in this area, it seemed that virtually every physical education researcher during the period from 1950 to 1970 at some time conducted a study to explore the relationship between motor performance and academic achievement or intelligence. Numerous approaches for testing the veracity of the various theories of integrated development have been used. A sampling of these will be presented. For the purposes of this article, the following categories of research strategies will be reviewed:

1. Comparison of the intelligence and/or academic achievement of athletes and nonathletes;
2. Comparison of the physical abilities of retardates and people of normal intelligence;
3. Correlation of motor and/or physical fitness with intellectual performance;

4. Experimental studies;
5. Physiological or neurological studies.

Comparison of Intelligence and Academic Achievement of Athletes and Nonathletes

A common type of investigation dealing with normal populations is that of comparing the academic performance of athletes and nonathletes, a type of study that was particularly prevalent in the 1960s and 70s. Eidsmoe (1951) and Lehsten (1964) conducted studies in which athletes' grades were compared with those of nonathletes. In both studies the athletes had higher grade point averages than did nonathletes. This relationship has been found to be generally true in most studies. However, there have been some conflicting results, such as those obtained by Davis and Berger (1973), who found no differences in GPAs between high school athletes and nonathletes.

Another strategy has been to compare the IQs of athletes and nonathletes. There has been less success at finding a positive relationship between athletic participation and intelligence. For example, Thorpe (1967) investigated the relationship between level of intelligence and success in badminton or tennis for 375 college women, and found no significant relationship between intelligence and success in these sports.

Slusher (1964) compared IQs, as measured by the Lorge-Thorndike test, of various high school athletic groups with 100 nonathletes. The athletic groups were 100 baseball players, 100 basketball players, 50 swimmers, 50 wrestlers, and 100 football players. The *nonathletic* subjects were reported to have significantly higher IQs than any of the athletic groups.

Rather than cite additional studies of this type, it might be more helpful to point out the obvious difficulties of making any firm conclusions in this particular area. The main difficulty in making comparisons with athletes is that the lower achieving individual is eliminated from the athletic group because he or she lacks the minimum grade point average that is almost always required for participation. This not only affects GPAs but might also affect average intelligence scores. Additionally, even if athletic groups are shown to have superior intelligence, it could be that their superior intelligence contributes to superior athletic performance instead of the other way around. Another difficulty is that, at all levels, athletes may be enrolled in different courses than nonathletes. And at the higher levels of education it is sometimes suspected that athletes are given breaks in grading that nonathletes do not receive.

Therefore, while the relationship between athletic and academic success has generally been shown to be modestly positive, little support can be found in this area of research to suggest that physical exercise directly enhances intellectual development.

Comparison of Physical Abilities of Retarded and Nonretarded Individuals

A great deal of research in this area has been devoted to comparing the physical ability of mentally retarded children with that of nonretarded children. Sloan (1951) compared each of the six scores on the Oseretsky Test of Motor Proficiency (OTM) obtained by 20 mentally retarded and 20 normal children 10 years of age. Each group contained an equal number of boys and girls. The six scores on the OTM were proposed to measure general static coordination, dynamic manual coordination, general dynamic coordination, speed, simultaneous movement, and synkinesia (precision of movement). An analysis of variance was used on each of the six measures. In all cases, there was a significant difference between the two groups at the .01 level. Furthermore, the significance was always in favor of the nonretarded subjects. No differences were found between sexes.

These findings were supported by Malpass (1960) when he compared 52 retarded children from an institution, 56 retarded children in public schools, and 71 normal children on their scores on the Lincoln revision of the Oseretsky Test. No significant differences were found between scores of the two retarded groups, but highly significant differences were found when the scores of either group were compared with those of the nonretarded group, the differences being in favor of the latter.

Thurstone (1959) found that mentally handicapped children were consistently inferior in performance of gross motor skills to normal children of comparable age. She found significant differences for each sex between these two groups on the following items: tennis ball throw for distance, volleyball punt for distance, standing broad jump, tennis ball throw for accuracy, side-stepping, 40-yard run, and right and left hand grip strength.

Heath (1942), using 170 mentally retarded boys, found a significant correlation (.66) between rail-walking performance and mental age for endogenous (hereditary) mentally retarded children. However, this relationship did not hold true for exogenous (nonhereditary) mentally retarded children. Thus he demonstrated the possibility of using performance on this test for the etiological classification of mentally retarded children.

In another study, Francis and Rarick (1959) studied 284 mentally retarded boys and girls ages 8 to 14. The children were given a number of motor tests that were classified as measures of static strength, running speed, power, balance, and agility. For each sex it was concluded that age trends in all the measures followed approximately the same pattern as those for normal children, but at a lower level for every age. The means of both boys and girls on most measures were 2 to 4 years behind the published norms of normal children. In addition, the discrepancy tended to increase with each advancing age level. However, when intelligence as measured was correlated with the motor performance items, the relationship was generally positive but low, and of approximately the same order as other investigators have reported with normal children (.10 to .30).

Howe (1959), in comparing 43 normal children and 43 retarded children (31 boys and 12 girls in each group) on 11 motor tests, reported almost universally significant differences in favor of the normal children. Analyses of variance showed that the normal boys performed significantly better than the retarded boys on the Sargent jump test, balance on one foot, tracing speed, tapping speed, dotting speed, grip strength, zig-zag run, 50-yard dash, squat-thrust, ball throw for accuracy, and paper and pencil maze tracing. The same held true for girls except for grip strength and ball throw for distance, in which no significant differences were found.

Sengstock (1966) compared the physical fitness of 30 educable mentally retarded boys (EMR) with two groups of normal boys: an older normal (ON) of 30 whose ages ranged from 120 to 180 months and a younger normal group (YN) of 30 whose ages ranged from 60 to 160 months. The measures used for physical fitness were the scales on the AAHPER Youth Fitness Test Battery. The ON group was significantly superior to the EMR group on all seven tests of physical fitness. However, the EMR group was significantly superior to the YN group on all the tests except the pull-ups and sit-ups. The investigator suggested that this second result may have been contaminated by an overwhelming advantage the EMR group had over the YN group in height and weight.

From the review above, it can be concluded that generally a positive relationship between motor and intellectual performance does exist when comparing retarded children with those from a normal population.

Correlating Motor and Intellectual Performance

A plethora of research studies have investigated the relationship among the results of various motor physical fitness tests and intellectual or academic achievement measures in normal populations. Several investigators have studied the relationship between physical growth and the intellectual domain. Klausmeier and his colleagues (Klausmeier, 1958; Klausmeier, Breeman, & Lehmann, 1958; Klausmeier & Check, 1959; Klausmeier & Feldhusen, 1964; Klausmeier, Feldhusen, & Check, 1959; Klausmeier, Lehmann, & Breeman, 1958; Gleason & Klausmeier 1958), working with children of various ages, investigated the relationships between physical growth and intellectual performance. They consistently found that the components of Olson's "organismic age," namely height, weight, grip strength, dental age, and carpal age, had very little if any relation to intellectual measures. Blommers, Knief, and Stroud (1955), in studying 120 preadolescent children, also concluded that the organismic age concept is of little use in discriminating among children of different intellectual levels. Likewise, Bayley (1956), in studying the profiles of children, indicates there is great independence among the components of growth used by Olson. It appears from these studies that physical growth measures are poor predictors of intellectual performance.

Many researchers have investigated the relationship between physical fitness and intellectual performance. Their studies usually included growth items as well as fitness variables, but they highlighted the fitness aspect. Jarman (1965) found consistently significant negative correlations between 21 tests measuring somatotype, maturity, body size, muscular strength and endurance, and motor ability and various academic achievement and intelligence measures. The subjects for his study were 109 boys 15 years of age. In addition, multiple correlations were computed with the nonintellectual variables serving as the predictors and the academic criteria as the dependent variables. Jarman concluded that although the multiple correlations between the physical variables and the academic achievement criteria were significant, they were still much too low to predict scholastic success from physical tests. The highest R^2 obtained was .31 between total grade point average and the physical variables, with the Wetzel physique channels and Sheldon's mesomorphy being the best predictors.

Miller (1962) correlated back strength, grip strength, leg strength, vertical jump, dodge run, and balance items with an index based on IQ and a semester examination for three age groups. These groups were 244 12-year-olds, 257 13-year-olds, and 228 14-year-olds. Some significant correlations were obtained between fitness items and the derived index. The correlations between vertical jump and the scholastic index for the three age groups were consistently positive, ranging between .21 for 12-year-olds and .20 for 13-year-olds. Any other significant correlations appeared for only one group, and the directions of these varied.

Disney (1963) compared 50 mentally gifted high school boys (IQs above 130) with a group of 50 boys of average intelligence (94-106) and comparable age on a number of fitness variables. The mentally gifted were significantly superior in the standing broad jump, 90-second sit-up test, 50-yard dash, softball throw, 30-second basketball shooting, Dyer tennis test, and Brady volleyball test. No differences were found between the groups on number of chin-ups, pass for distance, punt for distance, or Borleske 50-yard dash. In no case did the average group show significant superiority over the gifted group. Ray (1940) found consistently low but positive correlations between various fitness variables and mental ability measures on 432 high school boys.

Clark and Jarman (1961) established high and low groups of 20 boys each from 73 9-year-olds on three different strength tests (Roger's Strength Index, Physical Fitness Index, and Roger's Arm Strength Tests) and two growth measures (McCloy's Classification Index and the Wetzel Developmental Level). Extreme groups of 20 each were also established for each measure on 75 12-year-old boys and 69 15-year-old boys. Each pair of high and low groups was equated using IQs, and the academic achievements of the two groups were then contrasted. Clark and Jarman reported that there was a consistent and significant tendency for the high fitness groups to have higher means on both standard achievement tests and grade point averages. In addition, there were more and greater differences in scholastic achievement between the high and low Physical Fitness Index groups than there were for the other strength and growth groups compared.

Rarick and McKee (1949) made a case study of 20 normal third-grade children, 10 of whom exhibited a high level and 10 a low level of motor achievement. They concluded that the superior motor performers tended to be older, heavier, and stronger.

A great number of studies have shown little or no relationship between physical and/or motor fitness and intellectual performance. For example, Ryan (1963), using 80 male college students, found no difference between high and low achievement groups on stabilometer performance. Subjects were classified as high or low based on their performance on a college entrance exam. However, when grouped according to their achievement scores, overachievers (those whose grade average score was higher than their college entrance exam score) were found to score significantly higher than their counterparts on stabilometer performance. It was suggested that perhaps the motive to succeed in academic situations may be a more general characteristic than either intelligence or motor ability.

Hart and Shay (1964) reported that the correlations between the mathematical and verbal parts of the Scholastic Aptitude Test and the Physical Fitness indexes of 60 sophomore college women were not significant. However, the correlation between cumulative academic index and PFI scores was significant at the .05 level (r = .496). They concluded, "although physical fitness is not a general predictor of academic success, it is high enough to be considered as a necessary factor for the improvement of academic index in the general education of the college student" (p. 445).

Using 140 9-year-olds, 214 13-year-olds, and 133 17-year-olds, Day (1965) generally found insignificant correlations between various fitness, strength, and physique measures and IQ for all groups. The correlations that were statistically significant could not be considered as practically significant. For example, the correlation between 60-yard shuttle run and IQ for 13-year-olds was significant at the .05 level but was only .167. Similarly, Burley and Anderson (1955) found an insignificant correlation of .037 between jump-and-reach scores and Henmon-Nelson IQs for high school boys. Likewise, Johnson (1942) reported insignificant correlations between the Johnson Physical

Skill Test and IQ scores and academic grades with 310 college freshman men and women.

Sundholm (1965), using 66 7th- and 8th-grade girls, formed high and low intelligence groups on the basis of an IQ test. High and low achieving groups based on one semester's grades were also formed using the same subjects. The high and low groups were compared on the AAHPER physical fitness test and McCloy's General Motor Capacity Test (GMCT). There were no significant differences between the high and low intelligence groups nor between the high and low achievement groups on the AAHPER test. Furthermore, there was no difference between the high and low intelligence groups on the GMCT. However, there was a significant difference in mean GMCT scores between the high and low achievement groups.

The Medford Study in Oregon produced several studies that focused on the relationship between academic achievement and motor performance. For example, using 95 13-year-old boys, Broekhoff (1966) administered physique type, maturity, body structure, strength, and motor ability tests for the motor domain and the Otis and Stanford Achievement Tests for the intellectual domain. There was a noted absence of significant correlations between the intellectual and nonintellectual variables.

Ruffer (1965) compared the academic achievement of 50 highly active junior and senior high school boys with that of 50 physically inactive junior and senior boys. The active group had significantly higher academic averages and scored higher on the general intelligence scale than the inactive group.

Using this same basic plan, Biddulph (1954) divided 461 high school boys into high and low athletic achievement groups on the basis of the California Classification Plan. Then the two groups were compared on the Henmon-Nelson IQ, high school grade averages, and teachers' ratings of scholastic achievement. No difference was shown in IQ or achievement.

In a correlation study, Weber (1953) determined the relationships among scores on physical fitness, academic grade point average, entrance exam, and the nine scales of the MMPI obtained by 246 male college freshmen. The physical fitness score was a composite score made up of sit-ups for 2 minutes, 100-yard pick-a-back run, and 300-yard shuttle run. The only significant correlation found was between the fitness scores and grade point averages.

From the literature on normal populations reviewed thus far, conflicting conclusions may be drawn about the relationships between motor and/or physical fitness variables and intellectual performance, except for between physical growth items and intellectual performance, where there appears to be no relationship. Much of this conflict stems from a failure to clearly define what is meant by the physical or motor domain. Recognizing this dilemma, Ismail and Cowell (1961) defined the motor domain operationally by factor-analyzing 25 items that authorities claimed measure motor aptitude. They identified five factors: (a) speed and strength, (b) growth and maturity, (c) kinesthetic memory of the arms, (d) body balance on objects, and (e) body balance on the floor. The investigators felt that a shortcoming of this study was the absence of motor coordination items. Therefore, in follow-up studies coordination items were included and identified as an independent factor.

Using this definition of motor aptitude, Ismail, Kephart, and Cowell (1963) investigated the relationship between motor aptitude and intellectual performance. The subjects were 60 boys and 60 girls between 10 and 12 years of age classified into high, medium, and low achievement groups. Utilizing the factor analysis technique, the investigators extracted a factor which had high loadings on the Otis IQ, the Stanford

Achievement Test, coordination items, and some balance items. They concluded that this factor presents scientific evidence for seeing the individual as a whole in terms of the motor and intellectual domains. Furthermore, the authors were able to predict intellectual performance using motor aptitude test items. Repeating this basic study with a larger sample (122 boys and 89 girls in the 5th and 6th grades), Ismail and Gruber (1965a, 1967) factor-analyzed a wide variety of motor aptitude and intellectual achievement items. They were able to extract factors similar to those they had extracted before. Yoder (1968), in conducting a study similar to the ones by Ismail but with 195 boys and 145 girls in the 4th and 5th grades, found the same type of factors and relationships Ismail had reported. Thus, a further validation of the earlier studies was provided.

Following up the work in this area, Ismail and Gruber (1965a, 1967) further investigated the possibility of predicting intellectual performance from motor aptitude items. Regression equations for predicting IQ scores were developed for the total group, boys, girls, and high, medium, and low achievers. In addition, regression equations were developed on each group for the prediction of paragraph meaning, word meaning, arithmetic reasoning, arithmetic computation, and total achievement scores on the Stanford Academic Achievement Test. They concluded that the amounts of variance (R^2) associated with the several regressions are sufficient for either selection and/or prediction.

After developing the above regression equations, Ismail and Gruber (1965a, 1965b, 1967) investigated the relative contributions of different kinds of motor aptitude items in predicting intellectual items. They concluded that coordination items are generally the best predictors, followed by balance items, when estimating either Otis IQ or Stanford Achievement and subtest scores. Furthermore, they concluded that speed, power, and strength items have low and insignificant predictive power in estimating intellectual performance.

Dotson (1968), using the multivariate technique of canonical correlation, investigated the same relationships Ismail did. The findings with this multivariate technique were almost identical to Ismail's. Ismail's results were further validated across cultures when Ismail, Kane, and Kirkendall (1969) repeated the earlier studies using British children as subjects (48 boys and 46 girls). They concluded that the evidence shows a positive relationship between some motor aptitude items, especially coordination and balance, and well-established measures of intelligence and scholastic ability. This conclusion based on the testing of British children was similar in pattern to the one Ismail arrived at with American children in earlier studies. Therefore it served as a cross-cultural validation of the earlier results involving American children. Several other studies—by Kirkendall and Gruber (1970), Kirkendall and Ismail (1968), Gruber and Kirkendall (1970)—also confirmed the previous results by Ismail et al. when various multivariate techniques were used with other populations.

Finally, Thomas and Chissom (1972) found that the relationship between perceptual motor abilities and intellectual abilities was relatively strong for children in kindergarten and grade 1 but as age increased, the magnitude of this relationship decreased until the relationship was no longer present at grade 3. In a later study, the same authors (Thomas & Chissom, 1974) discovered that perceptual motor abilities were not successful predictors of future (1 year later) academic performance.

Experimental Studies

Unfortunately, there have been very few experimental studies of the actual effects of exercise and/or physical education upon intellectual development. Using the experimental approach, Gutin (1966) investigated the relationship between physical and intellectual performance. Fifty-five male students were randomly selected from a required physical education course and given a series of mental tasks, namely four tests of the Employee Aptitude Survey: verbal comprehension, visual pursuit, verbal reasoning, and symbolic reasoning. Of these students, 29 were given a 12-week program of physical exertion while the other 26 acted as controls. The mental tasks were administered again at the end of the 12-week period. No significant differences were found between the two groups at the end of the program.

In a somewhat similar investigation, McAdam and Wang (1967) investigated whether exercise facilitates the performance of a simple mental task. A group of 108 male adults was given a simple mental task consisting of associating letters of the alphabet with each of 16 different symbols, then subdivided into four treatment groups. Group 1 exercised vigorously for 10 minutes, Group 2 received typical classroom instruction, Group 3 lay down and rested to soft music, and Group 4 took an immediate retest of a simple mental task. Following the 10-minute treatment period, the first three treatment groups were also administered an alternate form of the mental task. Using an analysis of variance on the second test scores, the investigators reported there were no significant differences among the four groups.

Ismail (1967) conducted an experimental study to investigate the relative effectiveness of an organized physical education program upon IQ and achievement scores. Two matched groups consisting of 71 preadolescent 5th- and 6th-grade children were selected according to six criteria including IQ and achievement. A four-level nested factorial design was applied to IQ scores and academic achievement scores, using the following four factors: gender, level of achievement, paired subjects, and group (experimental or control). It was found that the program had no effect on IQ scores but had a significantly favorable effect on academic achievement scores.

Soloman and Pangle (1966) investigated the effect of a structured physical education program on the physical and intellectual development and self-concept of educable mentally retarded (EMR) boys. Working with 41 boys 13 to 17 years of age who were enrolled in public school special education classes, they concluded that IQ scores were not significantly improved as a result of an 8-week physical education program. It should be emphasized that the program lasted for only 8 weeks.

Chasey and Wyrick (1970), in a study to determine the effects of a concentrated 15-week physical development program on the visual-perceptual-motor skills of 73 institutionalized EMRs age 12 years and 2 months, concluded that gross motor activities did not have a substantial influence on academic performance. Similarly, Tomporowski and Ellis (1984) concluded that a 7-month aerobic exercise program did not improve the IQs of institutionalized adult mentally retarded persons. By contrast, Skolnick (1981) reported that both an exercise program and a game activities period greatly enhanced the academic achievement of students in the 6th grade.

The results from this area, as in the other areas, are mixed. The main conclusion one can draw from this area of endeavor is a somewhat backhanded one. I know of no study that has shown that exercise hampered intellectual performance and/or development.

Physiological-Neurological Studies

Surprisingly, I have been unable to find a single study that examines the mind-body relationship from a physiological point of view or asks whether physiological changes in the brain occur with exercise that would also enhance intellectual development. Altman (1970) and his colleagues have come as close as anyone to pursuing this question in their work, which showed that the development of the cerebellum in rats can be affected by early environmental manipulation. The manipulation applied was handling, which is considerably different from exercise, but this finding at least indicates that possibly there is something to the basic tenet that exercise at the appropriate time of development will enhance intellectual development.

CONCLUSIONS

From the review of literature presented, the following conclusions seem to be warranted:

1. There is generally a moderate positive relationship between motor performance and intellectual performance, especially with motor performance involving cognitive processes such as coordination and balance tasks, rather than with strength, cardiovascular endurance, or flexibility tasks.
2. There is no evidence of a relationship between physical growth measures and intellectual measures.
3. The relationship between motor and intellectual performance is strongest at very early stages of development and gradually disappears with age.
4. There is no conclusive evidence, pro or con, on the actual effects that exercise has on intellectual development. This entire area of study has yet to be seriously explored.

Experimental field studies are critically needed here. Furthermore, I believe the physiological exploration of brain development in relation to exercise is the route that will finally give us some answers to this question.

Finally, I will deal with what I consider to be the most interesting question that arose in preparing this paper. During the 1950s and 1960s a great number of studies were conducted that explored the mind-body relationship. Since then we have seen an almost complete lack of studies in this area, in spite of the fact that most questions on this topic remain unanswered. My question is, Why? I believe there are several explanations:

1. What is meant by motor performance, exercise, and so forth has often not been well defined or measured, thus resulting in conflicting research results.
2. Intelligence and academic achievement have not always been well defined, also causing conflicting and confusing results.

3. Once some relationships were established, the needed experimental field studies became too difficult and unwieldy to design and conduct.
4. In the 1950s and 1960s, physical educators were grasping for ways to justify exercise and physical education programs. If it could be shown that activity programs contributed to intellectual development, then they would gain credibility and be justified. Many studies aimed at showing this were conducted during the 1970s. Now it has become increasingly evident and accepted that exercise and physical activity programs are justified and needed because of their *physical* benefits. Thus there has been no real need recently to prove that physical activity programs contribute to mental performance.

This last explanation seems most plausible to me. In closing, I will say there are valid research questions to be answered in this area, and I suspect that we may again see attempts at answering them.

REFERENCES

ALTMAN, J. (1970). Environmental influences on the development of the cerebellum and motor performance in rats. *Indiana University Sesquicentennial Symposium proceedings.* Indianapolis: Indiana State Board of Health.

BAYLEY, N. (1956). Individual patterns of development. *Child Development, 27,* 45-74.

BIDDULPH, L.G. (1954). Athletic adjustment and the personal and social adjustment of high school boys. *Research Quarterly, 25,* 1-7.

BLOMMERS, P., Knief, L.M., & Stroud, J.B. (1955). The organismic age concept. *Journal of Educational Psychology, 46,* 142-150.

BROEKHOFF, J. (1966). Relationships between physical, socio-psychological, and mental characteristics of thirteen year old boys. Unpublished doctoral dissertation, University of Oregon, Eugene.

BURLEY, L., & Anderson, R.L. (1955). Relation of jump and reach measures of power to intelligence scores and athletic performance. *Research Quarterly, 26,* 28-35.

CHASEY, W.C., & Wyrick, W. (1970). Effect of a gross motor development program on form perception skills of educable mentally retarded children. *Research Quarterly, 41,* 345-352.

CLARK, H., & Jarman, B.O. (1961). Scholastic achievement of boys 9, 12, and 15 years of age as related to various strength and growth measures. *Research Quarterly, 32,* 155-162.

DAVIS, B.E., & Berger, R.A. (1973). Relative academic achievement of varsity athletes. *Research Quarterly, 44,* 59-62.

DAY, J.A. (1965). Relationships between intelligence and selected physical, motor, and strength characteristics of boys nine, thirteen, and seventeen years of age. Unpublished master's thesis, University of Oregon, Eugene.

DELACATO, H. (1959). *The treatment and prevention of reading problems.* Springfield, IL: Charles C. Thomas.

DELACATO, H. (1963). *The diagnosis and treatment of speech and reading problems.* Springfield, IL: Charles C. Thomas.

DISNEY, R.F. (1963). A comparative study of mentally gifted and average intelligence high school boys in physical education. Unpublished master's thesis, San Diego State College.

DOTSON, O. (1968). An investigation of multivariate test criteria and their application to integrated development components. Unpublished doctoral dissertation, Purdue University.

EIDSMOE, R.M. (1951). The facts about the academic performance of high school athletes. *Journal of Health, Physical Education and Recreation,* **32**, 20.

FRANCIS, R.J., & Rarick, G.L. (1959). Motor characteristics of the mentally retarded. *American Journal of Mental Deficiency,* **63**, 792-811.

GLEASON, G.T., & Klausmeier, H.J. (1958). The relationship between variability in physical growth and academic achievement among third- and fifth-grade children. *Journal of Educational Research,* **51**, 521-527.

GRUBER, J.J., & Kirkendall, D. (1970). Interrelationships among mental, motor, personality, and social variables in low achieving high school students with high intelligence. *Proceedings of the 73rd National College Physical Education Association for Men.* (pp. 35-42). Chicago.

GUTIN, B. (1966). Effect of increase in physical fitness on mental ability following physical and mental stress. *Research Quarterly,* **37**, 211-220.

HALL, S., & Lindsey, G. (1957). *Theories of personality.* New York: Wiley & Sons.

HART, E., & Shay, C.T. (1964). Relationship between physical fitness and academic success. *Research Quarterly,* **35**, 443-445.

HEATH, R. (1942). Railwalking performance as related to mental age and etiological type among the mentally retarded. *American Journal of Psychology,* **55**, 240-247.

HOWE, C.E. (1959). Comparison of motor skills of mentally retarded children and normal children. *Exceptional Child,* **25**, 352-354.

ISMAIL, A.H. (1967). The effect of an organized physical education program on intellectual performance. *Research in Physical Education,* **1**, 31-38.

ISMAIL, A.H., & Cowell, C.C. (1961). Factor analysis of motor aptitude of preadolescent boys. *Research Quarterly,* **32**, 507-513.

ISMAIL, A.H., & Gruber, J.J. (1965a). Predictive power of coordination and balance items in estimating intellectual achievement. *Proceedings of the 1st International Congress of Psychology of Sports* (pp. 744-772). Rome: Federacione Medico Sportiva Italiana.

ISMAIL, A.H., & Gruber, J.J. (1965b). Utilization of motor aptitude tests in predicting academic achievement. *Proceedings of the 1st International Congress on Psychology of Sports* (pp. 140-146). Rome: Federacione Medico Sportiva Italiana.

ISMAIL, A.H., & Gruber, J.J. (1967). *Motor aptitude and intellectual performance,* Columbus, OH: Charles E. Merrill.

ISMAIL, A.H., Kane, J., & Kirkendall, D.R. (1969). Relationships among intellectual and non-intellectual variables. *Research Quarterly, 40,* 83-92.

ISMAIL, A.H., Kephart, N., & Cowell, C.C. (1963). *Utilization of motor aptitude test batteries in predicting academic achievement* (Technical Report No. 1). West Lafayette, IN: Purdue University, Research Foundation.

JARMAN, B.O. (1965). Interrelationships between academic achievement and selected maturity, physique, strength, and motor measures of fifteen year old boys. Unpublished doctoral dissertation, University of Oregon, Eugene.

JOHNSON, G. (1942). A study of the relationship that exists between physical skill and intelligence as measured and general intelligence of college students. *Research Quarterly, 13,* 57-59.

KEPHART, N.C. (1960). *The slow learner in the classroom.* Columbus, OH: Charles E. Merrill.

KIRKENDALL, D.R., & Gruber, J.J. (1970). Canonical relationships between the motor and intellectual domains in culturally deprived high school pupils. *Research Quarterly, 41,* 496-502.

KIRKENDALL, D.R., & Ismail, A.H. (1968). The discriminating power of non-intellectual variables among three discrete intellectual Groups. *Contemporary psychology of sport: Proceedings of the 2nd International Congress of Sports Psychology* (pp. 451-488). Washington, DC.

KLAUSMEIER, H.J. (1958). Physical, behavioural, and other characteristics of high- and lower-achievement children in favored environments. *Journal of Educational Research, 51,* 573-582.

KLAUSMEIER, H.J., Breeman, A., & Lehmann, I.J., (1958). Comparison of organismic age and regression equations in predicting achievements in elementary schools. *Journal of Education Psychology, 49,* 182-186.

KLAUSMEIER, H.J., & Check, J. (1959). Relationships among physical, mental achievement and personality measures in children of low, average and high intelligence at 113 months of age. *American Journal of Mental Deficiency, 63,* 1059-1068.

KLAUSMEIER, H.J., & Feldhusen, J.F. (1964). Organismic development: Relationships among physical, mental, achievement, personality, and sociometric measures. *A report—Symposium on integrated development* (pp. 35-45). Purdue University.

KLAUSMEIER, H.J., Feldhusen, J., & Check, J. (1959). *Analysis of learning efficiency in arithmetic of mentally retarded children in comparisons with children of average and high intelligence.* Madison: University of Wisconsin, School of Education.

KLAUSMEIER, H.J., Lehmann, I.J., & Breeman, A. (1958). Relationships among physical, mental, and achievement measures in children of low, average and high intelligence. *American Journal of Mental Deficiency, 63,* 647-656.

LEHSTEN, N.G. (1964). A study of selected growth and development measures and their relationships to the achievement of boys in grades 7-12. Paper presented at AAHPER Convention, Washington, DC.

MALPASS, L.F. (1960). Motor proficiency in institutionalized and non-institutionalized retarded children and normal children. *American Journal of Mental Deficiency,* **64,** 1012-1015.

McADAM, E., & Wang, K.Y. (1967). Performance of a simple mental task following various treatments. *Research Quarterly,* **38,** 208-212.

MILLER, J.O. (1962). A study of the relationship between certain fitness variables and an index of scholastic standing in a selected sample of N.S.W. public secondary school children. Unpublished master's thesis, University of Sydney, Australia.

OLSON, W.C. (1949). *Child development,* Boston: D.C. Heath.

RARICK, G.L., & McKee, R. (1949). A study of twenty third-grade children exhibiting extreme levels of achievement on tests of motor proficiency, *Research Quarterly,* **20,** 142-152.

RAY, H.C. (1940). Interrelationships of physical and mental abilities and achievements of high school boys. *Research Quarterly,* **11,** 129-141.

RUFFER, W.A. (1965). A study of extreme physical activity groups of young men. *Research Quarterly,* **36,** 183-196.

RYAN, E.D. (1963). Relative academic achievement and stabilometer performance. *Research Quarterly,* **34,** 185-190.

SENGSTOCK, W.L. (1966). Physical fitness of mentally retarded boys. *Research Quarterly,* **37,** 113-120.

SKOLNICK, S.J. (1981). The effects of physical activities on academic achievement in elementary school children. Unpublished doctoral dissertation, Temple University.

SLOAN, W. (1951). Motor proficiency and intelligence. *American Journal of Mental Deficiency,* **55,** 394-406.

SLUSHER, H.S. (1964). Personality and intelligence characteristics of selected high school athletes and non-athletes. *Research Quarterly,* **35,** 539-545.

SOLOMON, A.H., & Pangle, R. (1966). The effects of a structured physical education program on physical, intellectual, and self-concept development of educable retarded boys. *Institute on Mental Retardation and Intellectual Development Behavioral Science* (Monograph No. 4).

STEINHAUS, A. (1964). The role of motor in mental and personality development. *A Report-Symposium on Integrated Development.* Purdue University.

SUNDHOLM, I. (1965). Physical fitness and motor ability scores of high and low achieving junior high school girls. Unpublished master's thesis, Central Michigan University.

THOMAS, J.R., & Chissom, B.S. (1972). Relationships as assessed by canonical correlation between perceptual-motor and intellectual abilities for pre-school and early elementary age children. *Journal of Motor Behavior,* **4,** 23-29.

THOMAS, J.R., & Chissom, B.S. (1974). Prediction of first grade academic performance from kindergarten perceptual-motor data. *Research Quarterly,* **45,** 148-153.

THORPE, J.A. (1967). Intelligence and skill in relation to success in singles competition in badminton and tennis. *Research Quarterly,* **38,** 119-125.

THURSTONE, T.G. (1959). *An evaluation of educating mentally handicapped children in special classes and in regular classes.* Cooperative Research Project Contract Number, OE - SAE - 6452, of the U.S. Office of Education, The School of Education, University of Carolina, Chapel Hill.

TOMPOROWSKI, P.D., & Ellis, N.R. (1984). Effects of exercise on the physical fitness, intelligence, and adaptive behavior of institutionalized mentally retarded adults. *Applied Research in Mental Retardation,* **5,** 329-337.

VAN DALEN, D.B., & Bennett, B.L. (1971). *A world history of physical education: Cultural, philosophical, comparative* (2nd ed.). Englewood Cliffs, NJ: Prentice-Hall.

WEBER, R.J. (1953). Relationship of physical fitness to success in college and to personality. *Research Quarterly,* **24,** 471-474.

YODER, J.H. (1968). The relationship between intellectual and non-intellectual performance. Unpublished doctoral dissertation, Purdue University.

Children in Physical Activity:
Motor Learning Considerations

Robert N. Singer
The Florida State University

The orientation and thrusts of cognitive scientists, cognitive psychologists, and information processing theorists and researchers in more recent years have had a considerable impact on motor learning scholars. Perhaps Connolly's (1970) work in this regard stands out in providing the impetus for focusing on the development of processes and mechanisms associated with motor skill in children.

Interestingly enough, prior to the Connolly publication the relationship of developing cognitive processes to motor learning/performance potential did not receive much attention in the literature. What children could perform physically was reported. Achievements in various gross motor skills (athletic activities) as well as isolated laboratory motor tasks were noted, contrasting the sexes and various age groups. Thus, normative-descriptive data were established. Thomas and French (in press) have updated this literature with meta-analysis in order to determine gender and age differences in motor performance during childhood and adolescence.

But not analyzed was *how* children learned. What processes and mechanisms are used to master challenging tasks? How are they developed? How do they function at different stages of maturational development? When is a child ready to learn a particular motor task? What about individual differences in rate of maturation, learning capabilities, and learning (cognitive) styles?

These are challenging questions. In order to answer them, we need to know what is involved in the learning of different kinds of motor skills. We should know what capabilities children possess at different stages of maturation. Attentional, perceptual, memorial, and decision-making processes are of special interest. We might then be able to determine to what degree the operation of internal process can be enhanced. The ultimate objective is to determine what kinds of learning situations and strategies seem to benefit most children, and how we can accommodate important differences in individual characteristics.

This direction of thinking and action is with us now to some degree (e.g., see Kelso & Clark, 1982; Keogh & Sugden, 1985, chaps. 12 and 13; Singer, 1980b, chap. 9; Thomas, 1984, chap. 4). Such preoccupations are likely to increase in the future. What the child does motorically is relatively easy to observe and assess. What contributes to such actions, and how such operations can be improved, is much more difficult to understand. The challenge is formidable for motor behavior scholars. Indeed, the challenge may be even greater for those directly responsible for the learning experiences of children.

With such thoughts in mind, I will describe (a) information processing perspectives with regard to children and classes of psychomotor tasks, (b) learning capabilities of children, and (c) implications for instruction and learning.

INFORMATION PROCESSING PERSPECTIVES

What a child is able to do, and do well, is obviously a function of an incredible number of factors. Information processing considerations lead us to realize that many processes governing situational and internal information contribute to motor performance. As Fitts (1964) points out, "skilled perceptual-motor performance can be viewed as involving operations such as information translation, information transmission, information reduction, information collation, and in some cases the generation of movement....Information storage (memory) is also involved of course" (p. 248).

If motor behaviorists are to contribute to an understanding of such matters, they need to adopt a process-oriented approach in their scientific work. This may be more easily said than done. For many years, most motor learning specialists believed that the study of movement itself was our unique contribution to the scholarly literature dealing with behavior. The analysis of cognitive factors (processes and strategies), they thought, should be undertaken by others such as cognitive psychologists. This was felt in spite of the fact that learning and performing complex motor activities involves a high degree of cognition.

Fortunately, the tide is turning. Various information processing models have been proposed (e.g., Marteniuk, 1976; Singer, 1980b; Welford, 1968; Whiting, 1972), and although they differ in technicalities and emphasis, fundamentally they are quite similar. Putting it simply (Singer, 1982), skill is a function of input (sensory-perceptual operations), central processing (organizing and managing information as well as consequent problem-solving and decision-making), and output (motor functions and feedback utilization). Beyond this basic pattern, skill is also enhanced by supportive psychological and physical characteristics, body composition, and a level of fitness sufficient to achieve the desired outcome.

Looking at matters in a more complex way, Figure 1 illustrates the potential mechanisms and processes involved in learning and performing a complex motor act. The sequence of operations shown appears to be initiated by most people. Differences in achievement among individuals can be partially explained in the way these operations function. The more skilled or faster learners in a particular activity have probably developed strategies that facilitate the operation of these processes. In other words, their movement production is better because their internal processes function better. Figure 2 indicates some major factors that contribute to the manner in which information processing activities may be expected to operate. As can be observed, developmental dynamics constitute one such factor.

Through normal development and maturation, children become better able to analyze situations, select pertinent cues, organize and generate plans for a movement or series of movements, and use ongoing feedback as available. But as research indicates, children at various ages can *learn* to improve their information processing capabilities. They can learn how to select, manage, and process information more effectively—to make their capacities more functional—within their developmental limitations.

This point suggests that we need to know more about the role of cognitive processes in motor performance and how young learners can best use their cognitive capabilities

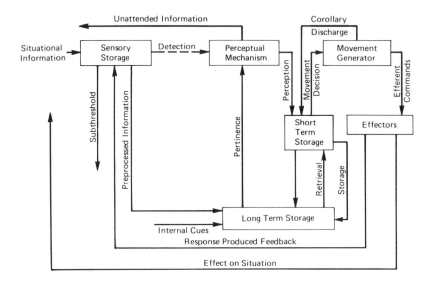

Figure 1—A conceptualization of information processing and motor behavior. *Note.* **From** *Motor Learning and Human Performance* **(3rd ed.) by R.N. Singer, 1980, New York: Macmillan.**

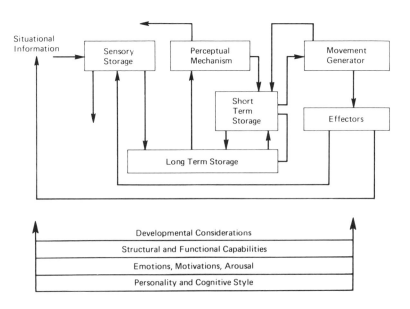

Figure 2—The effect of individual differences on the human behaving system. *Note.* **From** *Motor Learning and Human Performance* **(3rd ed.) by R.N. Singer, 1980, New York: Macmillan.**

while learning and performing motor skills (Singer & Gerson, 1979). More specifically, such processes should be facilitated by the learner's use of appropriate strategies (Singer, 1980a). Although strategies can be provided by an instructor, appropriate self-initiated strategies are more desirable. Alternative strategies, or options, are typically available to a learner in any achievement-oriented situation. Newell and Simon (1972) describe an effective strategy as the simplest and most efficient means of processing information in a situation. It governs the process of learning, according to Gagné (1985). Let us examine some internal activities related to learning and achievement.

LEARNING CAPABILITIES

First of all, irrespective of special strategy training, each child generally becomes better at complex motor skills with increased age, development, and experience. Learning procedures associated with growth and development as related to movement activities have been explained elsewhere (e.g., Singer, 1980b).

The level of proficiency attained in any task depends upon the functioning and integration of a number of processes, namely, the ability to

1. attend to relevant situational information;
2. make sense of the information available, using previously stored information (experience) as reference;
3. make appropriate decisions as to response selection;
4. process information, make decisions, and react as quickly as the task demands;
5. monitor relevant feedback; and
6. refine and adapt responses to situational dictates in order to perform successfully.

Obviously, the learning and performing of specific sport skills will depend in part upon the maturity of the child's nervous and muscular systems. Furthermore, what is taught and how it is taught will make a difference in the child's potential to achieve. Let us consider some of the more important internal processes and how they might be expected to function in the young. Subsequently we will examine strategies that might be useful in enhancing internal information processing operations.

Attending

The concept of attention has come to mean different things because it is involved in various ways in the process of learning, from cue discrimination to response selection (Singer, 1980b). One aspect of attention is degree of focus or distribution, whereby the person either attempts to take in a wide range of information or concentrates on one source. Another aspect has to do with degree of alertness, how quickly and easily the person attends to relevant cues. A third dimension of attention is associated with selectivity. The person shifts focus to the most meaningful and less important cues from moment to moment during a given activity. All of these characteristics of attention are environmental reactions. Attention can also be focused internally, on internal states and perceived competence (Carver & Scheier, 1981), but this aspect of attention will not be dealt with here.

Attentional processes such as those associated with anticipation, scanning, concentration, and selectivity change functionally with growth and development as well as with experience. They control which cues or information enter the human system, in what form, and when, as well as controlling sequential information processing activities. Attention span, the ability to concentrate, and a flexible attentional scanning process (from a narrow focus to a broad one) are related to potential accomplishments in many sports and physical activities.

With regard to generalized age considerations, Ross (1976) states that the young child seems to be "captured by one aspect of the situation" (p. 53). Visual scanning is restricted until age 6. As a result of what has been termed overexclusive attention, incidental learning is low. Adaptive learning and problem-solving are hindered. Incidental learning seems to hit a peak at ages 10 to 12, when observational and perceptual capabilities are increasing. Afterward, selective attention dominates. In other words, the same cue can result in a different focus of attention, depending on the learner's age and developmental state.

According to Simon (1972), "attention cannot be increased or diminished; it can only be relocated" (p. 15). With age and meaningful experiences, children learn to allocate their attention through appropriate strategies. They learn that only the essential aspects of a task need be attended to, thereby freeing the limited attentional capacity to make quicker correct decisions. Similarly, this attentional control increases the potential for anticipation.

The potential to parallel-process or to quickly serial-process information seems greater in adults than in children. As such input functions improve with age, the ability to simultaneously release several responses (output) likely does so, too. Wickens (1974) suggests that "if children are thus more single channel than adults in processing input information, it is reasonable to conclude that they are likewise less capable of dividing attention between two simultaneous responses" (p. 752).

Attention as a control process regulates how information is processed. Internal control operations require attention, and demands for attention require capacity. Consequently, learners must learn how to use the most efficient operations. Since attention is presumably a fixed capacity, limits in processing ability may be due less to structure than to the young learner's ineffective processing strategies. Task training has been claimed to reduce developmental differences when performing tasks that require selective processing (Lipps Birch, 1978), and Stratton (1980) has called for the teaching of actual strategies for processing information.

Using Memory

Whether we view memory as two stages (short-term and long-term) or as one process in which the way and extent information is processed will determine its resultant depth (long-term nature), one observation seems to be substantiated in the literature. Strategies used will determine how well new material is learned (and therefore remembered). The content of the original learning in relation to subsequent tests of learning (memory) is also an important consideration; retrieval cues enhance performance on tests of memory.

As with the case of attention, it is believed that memory storage capacity does not increase with age (Chi, 1976). It only appears to increase as children get older and demonstrate more effective memory. But this improved memory, states Chi, is probably due to the learned use of such memory-relevant strategies as rehearsal, naming (verbal labeling), grouping information, and recoding. The processes involved in storing information in memory, retrieving it, and using it appropriately are better developed in older than younger children. As they develop, children can more adequately process information—and more complex information—simultaneously and continuously. Increasing control is demonstrated over thought, mediation processes, and actual movements.

Previous experience may facilitate or hamper present learning, all the more reason why all learning should be positive and constructive. Some scholars have even speculated that after about age 8 there is no truly new learning task. The challenge is probably to take earlier learning and to apply it in a new context. Or, one might have to incorporate prior similar learnings into a more complicated act. For example, the basic throwing pattern is the fundamental foundational block of the tennis serve, the overhead volleyball serve, the smash in badminton, and other sport skills. Children who have developed a smooth throwing pattern and who realize its place in the context of learning a selected, more sophisticated act should be able to acquire skill with good success. It is one thing to have experienced foundational movements related to the learning of more complex skills, but another thing to perceive the relationship between present and past learning. The child may need guidance in this regard.

As for learning a so-called "new" activity, a young person may have certain advantages or disadvantages compared to an adult learner. Due to limited experience, a child has not built up a store of memory representations or overlearned associations that might conflict with present intentions. A child of 5 may learn to ski quite easily because he or she does not associate it with fear, is not paralyzed with self-analysis, and is not negatively influenced by other learned movements. By contrast, the adult may be overcome with emotional blockage: a fear of getting hurt, looking bad, or failing. A mental blockage is associated with being vicariously familiar with the activity and overthinking about oneself and the situational requirements. There could also be a movement handicap in that the balance learned in other activities may interfere with the balance technique required in skiing.

And yet an adult is favored in many achieving activities due to his or her cumulative knowledge of associated strategies (Dansereau, 1983) that support information-processing activities and learning. Examples are problem-solving and reasoning, the ability to focus attention and concentrate, and the knowledge of how to evaluate oneself and use feedback. Thus, stored memory experiences can work for or against either the adult or the child.

Decision-Making and Preparing the Movement

The ability to make rapid and effective decisions, as required in certain sports, is related to stage of development and prior experience. Laboratory studies (e.g., Hodgkins, 1963) show that reaction time generally decreases with each year to age 26, with best times shown from about age 19 to 26, after which there is a slow and steady decline. Highly skilled, habit-like behaviors, as well as adaptive, problem-solving behaviors, are reflective of much stored experience. Some physical activity situations demand automated acts, others demand responses to changing and often unpredictable conditions.

In self-paced activities, there is time to preview, evaluate, decide, and respond. Examples are bowling, golf, archery, and serving in tennis. In externally paced activities, the circumstances pace the person. Reactions must often be made rapidly to other people or to objects. The younger the child, the more likely he or she will perform more effectively in self-paced activities.

Speed of processing depends on information load, response demands, and the learner's capabilities. It includes cue detection, cue recognition, decision-making, and movement initiation. Each of these processes may change in function at a different rate during the process of maturation (Keogh & Sugden, 1985). One way to reduce processing time is to increase the certainty of input information or the response to be generated. Thus, younger children would be expected to perform better in tasks containing more certainty and in which processing requirements are slower.

Decisions lead to movements intended to fulfill the objectives of the task and personal expectations. Scholars have proposed a number of alternative concepts as to how responses are organized. For example a goal-directed movement may be the result of the activation of a motor program, plan, schema, idea, or a coordinative structure, depending on one's perspective. In any case, as children get older they learn more sophisticated and efficient movement rules. They develop a more sophisticated hierarchical control system, which enables them to produce more complicated movements as appropriate for the situation.

The notion of schema (Schmidt, 1975) has been particularly appealing in regard to children in describing the effects of variable practice on achievement in a specific task. Schema relate to the acquisition of rules that structure the production of a movement. These movement schema are most likely acquired in early childhood (Shapiro & Schmidt, 1982). Rather than postulating the existence of specific internal commands for specific acts, movement programs (schema) are proposed to be generalized. Complex rules must be formed to govern them.

In support of schema theory, a typical study is designed in which one group of subjects practices variations of a task while another group constantly practices only one form of the task. Both groups are then tested on a so-called novel task within the same response class. Typically, the group with varied practice performs best (Carson & Wiegand, 1979; Pigott, 1979). However, as Wade (1982) observes, schema theory and other popular conceptualizations are limited in addressing certain characteristics of motor skill such as timing behavior. Children must learn to anticipate events and time their responses accordingly. This involves motion prediction (of self, object, or both) and timed selection and initiation of a response. How children develop such an ability is still open to conjecture.

Applying Feedback

Information is usually available to a person as a result of performance, either during and/or after it. Such information is necessary for improvement and will be helpful if the person knows what feedback to sample, when, and how to use it. Research indicates differences according to age in the use and benefit of externally supplied feedback (e.g., from a teacher). For instance, younger children will show greatest performance gains when they are given general information feedback, older ones when given precise quantitative feedback (Thomas, Mitchell, & Solomon, 1979).

In other words, younger learners are not sensitive to relevant task detail. They are also impatient (Newell & Kennedy, 1978) about attempting to try again right after receiving knowledge of results, without taking time to understand and use such information. These younger children have not developed the higher order cognitive capabilities needed for knowing how to interpret and use highly specific feedback information. However, they can learn reasonably well to use the sources of feedback available, whether self-generated or externally supplied. Gallagher and Thomas (1980), for example, had children take the time to use knowledge about previous performance, which resulted in greater improvement.

IMPLICATIONS FOR INSTRUCTION AND LEARNING

Movement behaviors are influenced by personal perceptions and reactions. Internal processes serve to regulate what information is taken in by the system, how it is transmitted, and how decisions are made that lead to the organization of observable movements in a particular situation. These processes are activated in a similar fashion within all human beings. Differential functioning of any given process may be attributed to differences in maturation, experience, and acquired learning. This helps to account for variations in learning and performance among individuals.

The study and understanding of the information processing capabilities of developing individuals helps us to determine learning and performance potential. Expectations thus become more realistic. Instruction becomes more appropriate because it is systematically designed to consider the nature of the learners and of the activities to be acquired.

At present, most instruction in physical education is content-based. Movement and sport skills are taught with consideration of body mechanics and physical condition. The physical and motoric aspects of movement are of greatest concern. In this paper the attempt has been to stress, as equally important if not more so, the cognitive aspect of learning skills. Planning for instruction must consider content as well as those learner processes involved in the act of learning. And with young learners, these processes are activated and operate in ways somewhat dissimilar to the cognitive processes of adults.

Task analysis should reveal informational characteristics, response organization required, and feedback availability (Singer & Cauraugh, 1984). Learner analysis should indicate capability to process information and to control internal activities related to achievement. Furthermore, pertinent strategies to improve processing activities can be learned, to a certain degree, by children. Stage of development may be a limiting factor, but it appears that children are more capable of learning and applying appropriate strategies than was previously thought.

In support of this point, basically two approaches have been used. One is that different age groups of children are compared in their ability to demonstrate a particular strategy relevant to success in a task. The researcher arranges task conditions so that the subject can only perform well by responding to the task requirements with the strategy of interest. For example, Sugden (1980) used a positioning task with three age groups of boys: 6, 9, and 12 years. Retention intervals of 10 and 30 seconds were filled with interpolated activity or designated at rests. The 6-year-olds performed more poorly than the other two groups, presumably because they did not use a rehearsal strategy during the rest periods.

The other approach is to trace a treatment group in the use of a particular concept or strategy, using a control group as a reference. Again, comparisons can be made across different age groups to determine the ability of children to acquire a strategy and apply it to a criterion learning task. Bos and Mechling (1982) noted that children in grades 1 through 3 who were given special training to understand and use cognitive processes in learning the activity of throwing a ball between the legs, against a wall, and catching it made significant performance progress. The special training included structural insight into the nature of the task and self-regulated practice.

Many so-called adult learning strategies can probably be taught in a modified format considering the child's maturational stage. This principle is similar to the belief that many sport skills can be made less complex and more compatible with a child's capabilities, thereby increasing the probability of achievement. Future research will delineate the most favorable strategies that children can acquire for the learning of motor activities.

Perhaps we should end on an optimistic note tempered with a cautious reminder. The theme of this paper has been that internal control processes can be identified in a systems model, indicating how children behave in a systematic way. Further, information processing activities are strongly involved with achievement of motor skills. The related fields of cognitive science, artificial intelligence, and cognitive psychology are associated with the intent of forwarding formal theory and logical models about behavior. Presumably, how internal operations function can be specified in a predictable manner. Indeed, developments are extraordinary and create much intellectual excitement and challenges for those responsible for guiding the learning of others.

And yet we should be aware of the limitations of our knowledge about how internal operations function. After a state-of-the-science article was presented in the March 1985 issue of *Science*, a follow-up article (Ross, 1985) in the same publication revealed many obstacles and shortcomings that still need to be overcome. Research on the logical rules of behavior has answered some questions, but much still needs to be explained. Internal operations are mediated by personal factors that differ among individuals. Background and experience, as well as each person's unique use of intuition and logic, influence behavior in a learning situation.[1] We may not function as systematically as some would like to believe.

For example, Hubert and Stuart Dreyfus concluded from their observations of fighter pilots and chess players that only novices proceed according to formal rules (Ross, 1985). People rely heavily on context and experience as they gain skill. Ross writes,

> Expert pilots, for example, don't think of themselves as flying an airplane but as simply flying. Chess masters don't analyze hundreds of board movements; they sense the right move popping into their heads. What guides them is not analytic thought, apparently, but intuitive response. (p. 51)

As we consider the learning capabilities and performance expectations of children, our instructional efforts might reflect the state of the science associated with information processing and control processes as related to a child's developmental state. But let us always appreciate the intangibles. Each child's dynamic personal characteristics result in unpredictable and often nonexplainable occurrences in the attempt to perceive, understand, and learn. Internal systems are complex, and similar from person to person only to a point. They are different just enough, in nonmeasurable ways, to make

---

[1]Indeed, most of the winter 1984 issue of the *Review of Educational Research* was devoted to original papers on research on the teaching and learning of reasoning skills.

us feel uneasy about accepting any formal doctrine of behavior, at least at this point in the 20th century.

REFERENCES

BOS, K., & Mechling, H. (1982). The influence of structural task information and self-regulation on the acquisition of a complex skill in relation to practice conditions and age. *Scandinavian Journal of Sports Science,* **4**, 57-61.

CARSON, L., & Wiegand, (1979). Motor schema formation and retention in young children: A test of Schmidt's schema theory. *Journal of Motor Behavior,* **11**, 247-251.

CARVER, C.S., & Scheier, M.F. (1981). *Attention and self-regulation.* New York: Springer-Verlag.

CHI, M.T.H. (1976). Short-term memory limitations in children: Capacity or processing deficits? *Attention and Cognition,* **4**, 559-572.

CONNOLLY, K.J. (Ed.). (1970). *Mechanisms of motor development.* New York: Academic Press.

DANSEREAU, D. (1983). Learning strategy research. In J. Segal, S. Chipman, & R. Glaser (Eds.), *Thinking and learning skills: Relating instruction to basic research* (Vol. 1). Hillsdale, NJ: Erlbaum.

FITTS, P.M. (1964). Perceptual-motor learning. In A.W. Melton (Ed.), *Categories of human learning.* New York: Academic Press.

GAGNÉ, R.M. (1985). *The conditions of learning* (4th ed.). New York: Holt, Rinehart & Winston.

GALLAGHER, J.D., & Thomas, J.R. (1980). Effects of varying post-KR intervals upon children's motor performance. *Journal of Motor Behavior,* **12**, 42-46.

HODGKINS, J. (1963). Reaction time and speed of movement in males and females of various ages. *Research Quarterly,* **34**, 335-343.

KELSO, J.A., & Clark, J.E. (Eds.). (1982). *The development of movement control and coordination.* New York: Wiley.

KEOGH, J., & Sugden, D. (1985). *Movement skill development.* New York: Macmillan.

LIPPS BIRCH, L. (1978). Baseline differences, attention, and age differences in time-sharing performance. *Journal of Experimental Child Psychology,* **25**, 505-513.

MARTENIUK, R.G. (1976). *Information processing in motor skills.* New York: Holt, Rinehart & Winston.

NEWELL, A., & Simon, H.A. (1972). *Human problem solving.* Englewood Cliffs, NJ: Prentice-Hall.

NEWELL, K., & Kennedy, J. (1978). Knowledge of results and children's motor learning. *Developmental Psychology,* **14**, 531-536.

PIGOTT, R.E. (1979). *Motor schema formation in children: An examination of the structure of variability in practice.* Unpublished master's thesis, UCLA.

ROSS, A.O. (1976). *Psychological aspects of learning and reading disorders.* New York: McGraw-Hill.

ROSS, F. (1985). The black knight of A1. *Science, 6,* 46-51.

SCHMIDT, R.A. (1975). A schema theory of discrete motor skill learning. *Psychological Review, 82,* 225-260.

SHAPIRO, D.C., & Schmidt, R.A. (1982). The schema theory: Recent evidence and developmental implications. In J.A.S. Kelso & J.E. Clark (Eds.), *The development of movement control and coordination.* New York: Wiley.

SIMON, H.A. (1972). On the development of the processor. In S. Farnham-Diggory (Ed.), *Information processing in children.* New York: Academic Press.

SINGER, R.N. (1980a). Motor behavior and the role of cognitive processes and learner strategies. In G.E. Stelmach & J. Requin (Eds.), *Tutorials in motor behavior.* Amsterdam: North-Holland Publ. Co.

SINGER, R.N. (1980b). *Motor learning and human performance* (3rd ed.). New York: Macmillan.

SINGER, R.N. (1982). *The learning of motor skills.* New York: Macmillan.

SINGER, R.N., & Cauraugh, J. (1984). Generalization of psychomotor learning strategies to related psychomotor tasks. *Human Learning, 3,* 215-225.

SINGER, R.N., & Gerson, R.F. (1979). Learner strategies, cognitive processes, and motor learning. In H.F. O'Neil and C.D. Spielberger (Eds.), *Cognitive and affective learning strategies.* New York: Academic Press.

STRATTON, R.K. (1980). Strategic allocation in information processing: A developmental perspective. In R. Nadeau, W. Halliwell, K. Newell, & G. Roberts (Eds.), *Psychology of motor behavior and sport–1979.* Champaign, IL: Human Kinetics.

SUGDEN, D.A. (1980). Developmental strategies in motor and visual motor short-term memory. *Perceptual and Motor Skills, 51,* 146.

THOMAS, J.R. (Ed.). (1984). *Motor development during childhood and adolescence.* Minneapolis: Burgess.

THOMAS, J., & French, K.E. (in press). Gender differences across age in motor performance: A meta-analysis. *Psychological Bulletin.*

THOMAS, J.R., Mitchell, B., & Solomon, M.A. (1979). Precision knowledge of results and motor performance: Relationship to age 50. *Research Quarterly, 50,* 687-698.

WADE, M.G. (1982). Timing behavior in children. In J.A.S. Kelso & J.E. Clark (Eds.), *The development of movement control and coordination.* New York: Wiley.

WELFORD, A.T. (1968). *Fundamentals of skill.* London: Methuen.

WICKENS, C.D. (1974). Temporal limits of human processing: A developmental study. *Psychological Bulletin, 81,* 739-755.

WHITING, H.T.A. (1972). Overview of the skill learning process. *Research Quarterly, 43,* 266-294.

The Effect of Physical Activity
on Physical Growth and Development

Jan Broekhoff
University of Oregon

Since the effect of physical activity on the functional aspects of growth and development of children is dealt with elsewhere in this volume, this review is limited to the following structural areas: body dimensions and proportions, body composition, and maturation. One of the difficulties in assessing the effect of physical activity on growth and development lies in the definition of physical activity itself. For the purpose of this review, observations are made about (a) habitual levels of physical activity (including regular physical education), (b) additional or special physical education programs, and (c) intensive training programs in competitive sports.

In spite of the many studies that have been conducted to investigate the acute effects of exercise on structural and functional aspects of the human body, relatively little is known about the long-term influence of habitual physical activity levels and exercise programs on the growth and development of children and adolescents. As Cumming (1976) expressed it,

> A minimum of physical activity is likely necessary for optimal growth or development of children, but this minimum will likely never be known with certainty, just as the minimal activity patterns for the health of adults are likely to remain unknown. We cannot even define optimal growth and development, either in generalities or in specifics such as height, or heart volume, or maximum oxygen uptake. (p. 67)

A phenomenon that certainly appears related to optimal growth or development of children is the secular trend of accelerated maturation and increase in body size which began in many industrialized countries in the middle of the 19th century (see Malina, 1979, 1983a; Roche, 1979). In general, the trend is thought to be due to elimination of growth-inhibiting factors rather than to addition of growth-stimulating ones. Although some researchers still propose unicausal explanations for the trend (cf. Adams, 1981; Chiarelli, 1977), most investigators point to the interaction of a multitude of factors. The most prominently mentioned causes are better nutrition, improved health care and health status, improved socioeconomic conditions, increased urbanization, and genetic factors. In some western countries, the trend has now either slowed down or stopped altogether (Malina, 1983a).

Interestingly, exercise or physical activity is seldom mentioned as a contributor to this secular trend. Malina (1979) includes exercise among the factors that have created better living conditions but acknowledges at the same time that levels of habitual physical activity may have decreased as a result of industrialization. It would be difficult, therefore, to urge that the trend was caused in part by higher levels of physical activity. Nevertheless, the changes in growth and development exhibited by the secular trend can serve as a yardstick in assessing the effect of various levels of exercise on the growth of children and adolescents.

BODY DIMENSIONS AND PROPORTIONS

It is not difficult to find diametrically opposed statements concerning the effect of exercise on body dimensions in the general physical education literature. This is especially true for physical activity involving intensive training for sport competition. Edington and Edgerton (1976), for example, write that "potentially beneficial effects of exercise on general body growth have been noted in healthy young boys and girls (late teens) who had engaged in strenuous physical exercise during their childhood: they grow taller and heavier with larger chest girths and knee joint widths" (p. 220). Here, physical activity is clearly presented as growth-promoting, but the reader is left without references to primary sources.

On the other side of the ledger is the statement of Paulac (1982):

> We have noticed over a long time the influence of intensive exercises on the joining cartilages, which brings on premature ossification, and of the hypertrophy muscles [sic], a real height reduction which is not expressed by the "genotype," that is to say the "initial plan" of the genetic programme. (p. 80).

Once again, this assertion that strenuous exercise serves as a growth-inhibiting factor is not corroborated by factual evidence.

The secular trend of accelerated growth from 1850 to 1960 led to an increase in stature of approximately 1.3 cm per decade at age 9, 1.9 cm at age 13, and .6 cm at adulthood (Roche, 1979). As discussed earlier, researchers did not link these increases in height to physical activity levels or improved exercise habits. At the same time, strenuous exercise is described in physical education literature as both growth-promoting and growth-inhibiting. What is the evidence with respect to stature and exercise?

Stature

Some of the generalizations about physical activity as a growth-promoting or growth-inhibiting factor may have been derived from older studies that have been reported in earlier reviews (Malina, 1969; Rarick, 1974). Adams (1938), for example, found that black women between the ages of 17 and 21 who had engaged in strenuous labor during childhood were taller, heavier, and had larger girths and bone widths than a control group of women who did not engage in heavy labor during youth. The problem with the Adams study and other ex post facto observations is that there is no guarantee the two groups of women were equivalent before the period of heavy work started. In fact, Adams indicated that the two groups were sampled from two entirely different socioeconomic milieux. The differences, therefore, may have been caused by other variables than the work load.

Similar reservations must be made with respect to a study by Kato and Ishiko (1966), who found 116 cases of obstructed epiphyseal growth in the lower extremities of Japanese children who engaged in hard labor. The researchers observed premature closure of the femoral, tibial, and fibular epiphyses and related this to compressive stress from heavy loads carried on the shoulders. As Malina (1969) indicated, however, the children came from a very poor environment with substandard nutrition. Even so, more than 97% of the children examined did not show symptoms of marked premature closure.

The overwhelming evidence from studies with equivalent control groups is that extra classes of physical education (Kemper et al., 1974; Shephard, Lavelle, Jequier, Rajic, & LaBarre, 1980), special physical education programs (Coonan et al., 1982), or more strenuous physical training (Parizkova, 1968; Wyznikiewicz-Kop & Kobuszewska, 1980) do not affect growth in stature. In the Kemper study, students received two extra classes of physical education a week over a 1-year period; Shephard reported on the Trois-Rivières regional experiment in which children received four extra physical education classes per week over an 8-year period. Coonan reviewed a number of Australian research projects in which the effects of fitness training and skills treatment were studied. Parizkova followed groups with varying levels of physical training and activity over a 4-year span, and Wyznikiewicz-Kop contrasted young athletes with nonathletes over a period of 3 years. Although significant findings were observed in functional variables in some of these studies with preadolescent and adolescent children, differences in stature were found to be insignificant.

Bone Width and Density

As Cumming (1976) noted, a lot more is known about the effect of inactivity upon bone growth and skeletal changes than about the effect of intense physical training. Although there are many examples of bone hypertrophy as a result of prolonged physical stress (e.g., the width of the dominant wrist and elbow in tennis players), it is still hard to tell whether active children have any skeletal advantages over relatively inactive children in later years (p. 68). Scientists in the Soviet Union and Yugoslavia have been particularly interested in sport-specific osteogenesis. In Leningrad, studies have been conducted both at the Pavlov First Medical Institute and the Lesgaft Institute of Physical Culture.

Rjazanova (1980) studied the skeleton of the hand and wrist roentgenographically and osteometrically in two groups of swimmers, ages 8 to 10 and 17 to 19 years. Both age groups showed accelerated synostosis compared to control groups of nonathletes. In the younger group the difference was attributed largely to a selection factor, as these children had not engaged in strenuous workouts for any length of time. Compared to basketball players, however, the older swimmers had significantly longer metacarpal bones of the left hand, but not of the right. The same was noted for the thickness of these bones. Whereas basketball players showed advanced development of the dominant hand, the older swimmers had uniform lengthening and thickening of the metacarpal bones of both hands.

Korneva (1979) compared two groups of volleyball players (13 to 14 years and 15 to 16 years old) to children who did not participate in competitive sports. For both age groups, the second metacarpal bone of the volleyball players was significantly longer than that of the controls. In the older group, the thickness of the compact bone layer of the metacarpals was larger in the athletes than in the controls. This greater thickness was accompanied by a narrowing of the osseomedullary canal. Volleyball players showed a delayed synostosis compared to controls. Kornev (1980) found a delayed ossification of the distal epiphyses of radius and ulna and the bones of the hand and wrist of male adolescent boxers and soccer players compared to basketball players of the same chronological age (15-17 years). Mineralization of the metacarpals, however, was most pronounced in boxers and least developed in soccer players. Prives and Aleksina (1978) stated that different kinds of sport have different effects on the ossification of the tubular bones. The process of synostosis, according to these researchers, depends not only on genetic factors but also on environmental ones including physical activity.

Several Yugoslavian studies have dealt with the influence of strenuous physical activity on the development of the pelvis. Kliment, Schmidt, and Zajac (1971), for example, concluded that competitive skiing does not affect the inner dimensions of the pelvis (parturient canal) adversely. In women who started ski training before the age of 15, however, the authors found a conjugata externa of less than 18 cm in 75% of the cases. In a control group of competitive swimmers, such low values were not found. In a later investigation, Kovacikova (1978) compared the external pelvic dimensions of three groups of women: competitive athletes, physically active nonathletes, and women who did not exercise. A statistically significant narrowing of the pelvis in all measured dimensions was observed in the competitive athletes when compared with the other two groups. The author attributed the difference to a combination of constitutional (selection) and environmental (physical exercise and sport) factors. The Yugoslavian authors expressed caution with respect to excessive physical stress for women during puberty.

Proportionality

Secular increase in height and other dimensions have been approximately proportional, so overall body shape and proportions have changed little (Charzewski & Bielicki, 1978; Malina, 1983a). Some studies (Eiben, 1978; Eveleth & Tanner, 1976) have reported a tendency toward smaller trunks and increasing linearity in the secular trend. Little evidence is available about the effect of exercise on body proportions. Warren (1980) observed that a group of adolescent ballet dancers who were studied over a period of 4 years had a significantly increased arm span and a decreased upper to lower body ratio compared to other female members of their families. She related these differences to a delayed menarche as a result of energy drain, although she did not rule out the possibility of selection. Parizkova (1968) found that boys classified in a high activity group had significantly lower ratios of pelvic width to height and shoulder width than boys in lower activity groups after the 4th year of observation. No significant differences were found during the first 3 years of the study. Since classification into activity groups occurred ex post facto, such differences should be interpreted with reservation. In general, there is little to suggest that even strenuous physical training affects body proportionality.

BODY COMPOSITION

The secular trend in body weight from 1850 to 1960 saw an increase per decade of .8 kg at 10 years of age, 1.8 kg at 15 years, and .9 kg at 20 years of age (Roche, 1979). Over approximately the same time span, Himes (1979) showed that the ratio of mean weight to stature for 9-year-old boys generally increased. Such changes may indicate merely a pattern of acceleration rather than a change in the relationship between body weight and stature, since the weight-height ratio for boys increases with age during normal development. Himes noted, however, that subcutaneous fat tissue has increased over the past decades. Evidence of this trend is supplied by Tanner and Whitehouse (1962, 1975) and more recently by the National Children and Youth Fitness Study (Pate, Ross, Dotson, & Gilbert, 1985). In these studies, the increase in subcutaneous fat appears to be more significant in the upper percentiles. Himes speculated that if fat tissue has increased at a faster rate than total body weight, then younger generations should have greater absolute strength (larger bulk) but less strength relative to body weight (smaller proportion of lean body mass). The secular trend in body composition is therefore not a desirable one.

Habitual Physical Activity

The increase in childhood obesity has often been linked to increased food intake coupled with a lack of physical activity. Automation in industrialized society and the appeal of television to children as well as adults have been mentioned as causes for a presumed decline in physical activity patterns. However, it is difficult to find objective evidence about the activity patterns of children and adults at various points in history. Kemper et al. (1983) and Verschuur et al. (1984) did establish that habitual physical activities of teenagers decline with age. In a carefully designed longitudinal study, they defined activity patterns as the "total activity time spent per week on physical activities with an energy expenditure of 4 METs [multiples of metabolic resting equivalents] or more" (1983, p. 211). Over a period of 5 years (ages 12 to 17), the activity time for girls dropped from 9.5 to 8 hours per week whereas the boys showed a decline from 10 to 7.5 hours.

When Kemper analyzed the activity patterns in terms of intensity, he found that girls actually increased their number of hours of light activities (4-7 METs) but spent little or no time in heavy activities (over 10 METs). Over the period of study, percentage body fat for girls increased from 23% at 12 years to 28% at age 17. Since girls normally increase their body fat percentage during adolescence, the increase could not be causally linked to the decline in heavy activity patterns. Boys during the same period maintained the same level of heavy activities. Their mean percentage body fat remained stable at 16% from ages 12 to 17.

The recent National Children and Youth Fitness Study included an extensive section devoted to activity patterns. Ross, Dotson, and Gilbert (1985) concluded on the basis of this study that approximately half of the American children in grades 5 through 12 do not meet the minimum weekly requirement of vigorous physical activity necessary for an effectively functioning cardiorespiratory system. This minimum weekly requirement is based on a position paper by the American College of Sports Medicine (1978) and modified somewhat in a report by the U.S. Department of Health and Human Services (1980). It recommends "exercise which involves large muscle groups in dynamic movement for periods of 20 minutes or longer, three or more times a week, and which is performed at an intensity requiring 60 percent or greater of an individual's cardiorespiratory capacity" (p. 79). One must remember, however, that these guidelines were originally drawn up for healthy adults and that they address mainly cardiorespiratory fitness.

Additional Physical Education

There is ample evidence that carefully designed activity programs can be effective in reducing percentage body fat in adults as well as children. Since 1977 a number of research projects investigating the effects of daily physical education programs have been conducted in various parts of Australia. Coonan et al. (1982) reviewed the results of the School Health, Academic Performance and Exercise Project (SHAPE) which involved more than 500 10-year-old boys and girls. Children in the control group received the regular physical education program of three half-hours per week of motor skills work; one experimental group participated in a fitness training program of 1 1/4 hours each day; and a third group took part in a skills treatment program of similar duration to the fitness training. After the 14-week experiment, children in the fitness training program showed a significant reduction in subcutaneous fat as measured by the sum of four skinfolds. Children in the skills program did not differ significantly from the controls on the skinfold variable. A follow-up study of SHAPE confirmed the effectiveness of the project but also indicated the need for close adherence to the exercise objectives.

Kemper et al. (1974) did not find significant differences in body composition between 12- and 13-year-old boys who received daily physical education for 1 hour and controls who had 3 hours of physical education per week. The extra 2 hours were an extension of the normal physical education program which aimed mainly at improving motor skills. The results of this Dutch study appear to corroborate the Australian findings that an increase in time alone may not produce significant changes in body composition. An additional Australian study, the so-called Body Owner's Project, focused on the use of health courses to improve physical health status. Children who were taught to monitor their activity behaviors and record them did gain health benefits, including reduced skinfold measures, over and above those arising from unmonitored daily physical education (Coonan et al., 1982, p. 241). Parizkova (1968, 1970) found that the differences among groups of boys with different physical activity patterns were most pronounced in body composition. After 4 years of longitudinal observation, boys in the highly active group had significantly less fat and more lean body mass than the boys in the low activity group. These groups of 15-year-olds had not shown any differences at the beginning of the study when they were 11 years old. She also reported on several successful summer camp programs that combined diet and exercise in the treatment of obese children (Parizkova, 1973).

Intensive Training Programs

As Cumming (1976) noted, physical exercise is important in childhood for weight control. Children who participate in competitive sports seldom show problems of obesity. Parizkova (1973) demonstrated significant differences in the body composition of young male and female athletes in various sports when compared with controls. Invariably, the young athletes had a lower percentage body fat and a larger percentage of lean body mass. Motajova (1974) showed similar differences over a 4-year longitudinal study between young athletes and children who only participated in school physical education. Since it is impossible to assign children randomly to control groups and athletic competition, comparisons between athletes and controls should be interpreted with caution. It is most likely the children with favorable physiques and body composition who will be drawn to competitive sports. Nevertheless, there is little question that strenuous training programs in combination with an appropriate diet will reduce the percentage of body fat. In such situations, the problems that arise are more often related to excessive leanness than to obesity.

MATURATION

One of the more remarkable features of the secular trend has been a pattern of accelerated growth. This aspect of the trend is best illustrated by the decrease in the age at menarche (the time of first menstruation). In many countries, age at menarche decreased at a rate of 4 months per decade from the middle of the 19th century until recently. There is no evidence that the trend of earlier maturation can be linked to changes in habitual physical activity patterns. Equally, there is no evidence that additional programs of moderate intensity influence the rate of growth of the skeleton and the reproductive system. In the area of competitive sports for children, however, the maturational question is important because in some sports delayed maturation has been observed, especially in girls.

Strenuous Training

As mentioned earlier in the section on body dimensions, there are widely divergent opinions about the effect of strenuous exercise on growth. Such opinions are reflected in the research literature. Evidence for accelerated growth in height as a result of a training program comes from a widely quoted study by Ekblom (1969) in which five subjects in the training group showed a greater height increase over a 32-month training period than a group of four control subjects. The design of this study and its small sample size hardly allow for any generalization. No skeletal age assessments were made for these early adolescent boys. If some of the experimental subjects were late maturers, that fact alone could explain the catch-up growth during the latter part of the study. Equally unconvincing is a report by Delmas (1981), who studied 11 girl and 8 boy gymnasts between the ages of 8 and 16 years over a period of 18 months. The author found a "break" in the growth curve of height in two-thirds of these children. This observation is confounded further by the fact that the young athletes were on an extremely restricted diet. Needless to say, there is a great need for controlled studies in this area.

Delayed Menarche

On the average, menarche occurs later in athletes than in the general population. This phenomenon has been observed for a number of sports, but cross-culturally it has been especially consistent in such sports as figure skating, gymnastics, long-distance running, and ballet. Swimmers appear to be an exception to this trend according to most of the observations in this area. An excellent review of menarche in athletes is provided by Malina (1983b), who also addressed the question of causation. Since it is impossible to design studies in which children are randomly assigned to competitive athletics, it is very difficult to isolate intense physical training as the primary cause for the phenomena of delayed menarche and amenorrhea. One of the strongest rival hypotheses is that of systematic selection. In a number of sports, late-maturing girls, for structural as well as functional reasons, have an advantage over early maturers. This is especially so in ballet, gymnastics, and certain events in track and field. In such sports, the process of selection would increasingly favor late-maturing girls at higher levels of competition.

The mechanisms by which strenuous training could influence the timing of menarche are not clearly understood. Frisch et al. (1974, 1976) postulated that a critical percentage of body fat (approximately 17%) must be reached before the onset of menstruation, and that 22% body fat is desirable for maintaining regular ovulatory cycles. Primary and secondary amenorrhea would thus be caused if, due to strenuous training, the percentage body fat dropped below these levels. This so-called critical weight theory, however, has not found universal acceptance (see Malina, Spirduso, Tate, & Baylor, 1978; Trussell, 1980). In a longitudinal study of early adolescent ballet dancers, Warren (1980) concluded that, in addition to low body weight and percentage body fat, an energy drain may have had a significantly modulatory effect on the hypothalamic pituitary set point at puberty, resulting in a prolonged prepubertal state and induced amenorrhea. Menarche in this group was significantly delayed in comparison to controls, occurring at a mean of 15.4 years. Warren noted that pubertal development accelerated for these girls during periods of planned or forced rest.

Frisch et al. (1981) found that the age at menarche in groups of 21 college swimmers and 17 runners was positively related to the number of years these women had trained premenarcheally. Each year of training before menarche delayed the onset of menstruation by 5 months. The mean age at menarche for the 20 athletes who started training postmenarcheally was 12.8, whereas the mean age for the 18 girls who started training before menarche was 15.1 years (p. 1560). Frisch et al. also noted significant differences between the pre- and postmenarcheal groups in cycle irregularity and amenorrhea. A similar observation was made by Levenets (1979) for 205 Russian adolescent athletes, 24.8% of whom had opsomenorrhea or secondary amenorrhea. Malina (1982) criticized the findings of Frisch et al. on the basis of the small and seemingly unusual sample of athletes (12 swimmers and 6 runners) who started training before menarche. The findings were unusual in that the age at menarche of swimmers in the majority of studies approximates the mean of the general population. Malina also pointed out that the correlation between age at menarche and years of premenarcheal training does not imply a cause and effect relationship.

The relationship between years of premenarcheal training and age at menarche appears to be corroborated in an overview by Märker (1981) in which menarcheal age is reported by sport and related to the beginning of training. The author observed that delayed menarche occurs more frequently in gymnastics, figure skating, and diving than in other sports. Since girls in these sports begin training at an earlier age than in other sports, there appears to be at least an inferred relationship between the age at which strenuous training begins and the age at menarche. Märker noted, however, that athletes with late menarche experienced no ill effects with respect to their reproductive functions, based on data gathered on childbirth. In spite of the differences in age at menarche among athletes in different sports, the age at parturition showed no predictable pattern. Gymnasts, who had the highest mean age at menarche, were among the youngest in age at parturition. The author concluded that fertility was not impaired by the intense training started during early childhood.

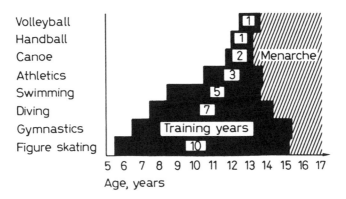

Figure 1—Number of years of training before menarche of female athletes from different sports (Märker, 1981).

CONCLUSIONS

If one thing became clear during the preparation of this brief overview, it was the difficulty of isolating the factor of physical activity and its effect on the growth and development of children and adolescents. Factors such as exercise should never be considered in isolation, as there is always a complex interaction of both genetic and environmental variables. This makes the design of controlled studies very problematic. Most of the studies reviewed relied on post hoc observations that allowed for a number of alternate explanations. There is no conclusive evidence that physical activity, even of high intensity and duration, markedly affects growth in stature and body proportions. Neither is there conclusive evidence that moderate or strenuous exercise during childhood accelerates the growth process. Research on female athletes presents some presumptive evidence that strenuous physical training before menarche delays the onset of puberty and prolongs the prepubertal stage. The mechanism(s) underlying this phenomenon are not clearly understood. Although fertility and reproductive functions do not appear to be endangered by strenuous physical activity before puberty, research findings of smaller pelvic dimensions and increased incidence of irregularity and amenorrhea need to be followed up in better-controlled investigations.

Habitual levels of physical activity of children and adolescents decline with age. Children who remain active in additional programs of physical education or competitive sport show the benefits of this training in a lower percentage of body fat and a larger percentage of lean body weight compared to more inactive children. To maintain or attain desirable standards of body composition, programs of physical education have to be carefully designed both with respect to duration and intensity. Australian and Dutch studies showed that merely increasing the length of time of traditional physical education programs will not of itself lead to desirable changes in terms of body composition. If time is limited, the emphasis of physical education programs should be on teaching activities that will be carried on after school. Experiments with daily physical education periods supported by physical health classes have shown that developmental and fitness objectives, including the control of obesity, can be reached if these programs are properly monitored and supported.

REFERENCES

ADAMS, E.H. (1938). A comparative anthropometric study of hard labor during youth as a stimulator of physical growth of young colored women. *Research Quarterly, 9*, 102-108.

ADAMS, J.F. (1981). Earlier menarche, greater height and weight—A stimulation stress factor hypothesis. *Genetic Psychology Monographs, 104*, 3-22.

AMERICAN College of Sports Medicine. (1978). Position statement on the recommended quantity and quality of exercises for developing and maintaining fitness in healthy adults. *Medicine and Science in Sports, 10*, vii-x.

CHARZEWSKI, J., & Bielicki, T. (1978). Is secular trend in stature associated with relative elongation of limbs? *Homo, 29*, 176-181.

CHIARELLI, B. (1977). On the secular trend of stature: A body-constitution interpretation. *Current Anthropology, 18*, 524-525.

COONAN, W., Worsley, T., Dwyer, T., Leitch, D., Daw, C., Hetzel, B., & Maynard, E. (1982). Daily physical education: A review of current Australian research projects. In M.L. Howell & J.E. Saunders (Eds.), *Movement and sport education: Proceedings of the VII Commonwealth and International Conference on Sport, Physical Education, Recreation, and Dance* (Vol. 6, pp. 239-245). Queensland, Australia: University of Queensland, Department of Human Movement Studies.

CUMMING, G.R. (1976). Child in sport and physical activity—Medical comment. In J.G. Albinson & G.M. Andrew (Eds.), *Child in sport and physical activity* (pp. 67-77). Baltimore: University Park Press.

DELMAS, A. (1981). Sur l'entrainement physique intense chez las enfants et les adolescents. *Bulletin de L'Academie Nationale de l'Embriologie, 165*, 121-126.

EDINGTON, D.W., & Edgerton, V.R. (1976). *The biology of physical activity*. Atlanta: Houghton-Mifflin.

EIBEN, O.G. (1978). Changes in body measurements and proportion of children, based on Kormend growth study. *Auxology: Human Growth in Health and Disorder,* **13**, 187-198.

EKBLOM, B. (1969). Effect of physical training in adolescent boys. *Journal of Applied Physiology,* **27**, 350-355.

EVELETH, P.B., & Tanner, J.M. (1976). *Worldwide variation in human growth.* Cambridge: Cambridge University Press.

FRISCH, R.E. (1976). Fatness of girls from menarche to age 18 years, with a nomogram. *Human Biology,* **48**, 353-359.

FRISCH, R.E., Gotz-Welbergen, A.V., McArthur, J.W., Albright, T., Witschi, J., Bullen, B., Birnholz, J., Reed, R.B., & Hermann, H. (1981). Delayed menarche and amenorrhea of college athletes in relation to age of onset of training. *Journal of the American Medical Association,* **246**, 1559-1563.

FRISCH, R.E., & McArthur, J.W. (1974). Menstrual cycles: Fatness as a determinant of minimum weight for height necessary for their maintenance or onset. *Science,* **185**, 949-951.

HIMES, J.H. (1979). Secular changes in body proportions and composition. In A.F. Roche (Ed.), Secular trends in growth, maturation and development of children, *Monographs of the Society for Research in Child Development,* **44**, 28-58.

KATO, S., & Ishiko, T. (1966). Obstructed growth of children's bones due to excessive labor in remote corners. In K. Kato (Ed.), *Proceedings of International Congress of Sport Sciences, 1964* (p. 479). Tokyo: Japanese Union of Sport Sciences.

KEMPER, H.C.G., Dekker, H.J.P., Ootjers, M.G., Post, B., Snel, J., Splinter, P.G., Storm-Van Essen, L., & Verschuur, R. (1983). Growth and health of teenagers in the Netherlands: Survey of multidisciplinary longitudinal studies and comparison to recent results of a Dutch study. *International Journal of Sports Medicine,* **4**, 201-214.

KEMPER, H.C.G., Ras, K.G.A., Snel, J., Splinter, P.G., Tavecchio, L.W.C., & Verschuur, R. (1974). *Invloed van Extra Lichamelijke Opvoeding.* Amsterdam: Posthuma & Snabel.

KLIMENT, V., Schmidt, P., & Zajac, J. (1971). Influence of physical exertion on the development of the pelvis. *Bratislavske Lekarske Listy,* **56**, 64-67.

KORNEV, M.A. (1980). The effect of some sports on the hand skeleton of children and adolescents. *Arkhiv Anatomii Gistologii,* **78**, 5-9.

KORNEVA, E.F. (1979). Certain peculiar features in the structure of the hand skeleton in young volleyball players. *Arkhiv Anatomii Gistologii,* **77**, 11-16.

KOVACIKOVA, J. (1978). Changes in dimensions of osseous pelvis in active sportswomen. *Ceskoslovenska Gynekologie,* **43**, 490-493.

LEVENETS, S.A. (1979). Characteristics of the physical and sexual development of girls regularly engaging in sports. *Gigiena i Sanitariia,* **1**, 25-28.

MALINA, R.M. (1969). Exercise as an influence upon growth. *Clinical Pediatrics,* **8**, 16-26.

MALINA, R.M. (1979). Secular changes in size and maturity: Cause and effects. *Monographs of the Society for Research in Child Development*, **44**, 59-102.

MALINA, R.M. (1982). Delayed age of menarche. *Journal of the American Medical Association*, **247**, 3312.

MALINA, R.M. (1983a). Secular changes in growth, maturation, and physical performance. *Exercise and Sport Science Reviews*, **11**, 203-255.

MALINA, R.M. (1983b). Menarche in athletes: A synthesis and hypothesis. *Annals of Human Biology*, **10**, 1-24.

MALINA, R.M., Spirduso, W., Tate, C., & Baylor, A.M. (1978). Age at menarche and selected menstrual characteristics in athletes at different competitive levels and in different sports. *Medicine and Science in Sports*, **10**, 218-222.

MÄRKER, K. (1981). Influence of athletic training on the maturity process. In J. Borms, M. Hebbelinck, & A. Venerando (Eds.), *The female athlete* (pp. 117-126). Basel, Switzerland: Karger.

MOTAJOVA, J. (1974). Effect of special stress over a four-year period on certain morphological parameters and bone age in growing children. *Folia Morphologica*, **22**, 358-361.

PARIZKOVA, J. (1968). Longitudinal study of the development of body composition and body build in boys of various physical activity. *Human Biology*, **40**, 212-225.

PARIZKOVA, J. (1970). Activity, obesity, and growth. *Monographs of the Society for Research in Child Development*, **35**, 28-32.

PARIZKOVA, J. (1973). Body composition and exercise during growth and development. In G.L. Rarick (Ed.), *Physical activity: Human growth and development* (pp. 97-124). New York: Academic Press.

PATE, R.A., Ross, J.G., Dotson, C.O., & Gilbert, G.G. (1985). The new norms: A comparison with the 1980 AAHPERD norms. *Journal of Physical Education, Recreation & Dance*, **56**, 28-30.

PAULAC, J. (1982). The discovery and selection of young sportsmen and their intensive training: Origins and dangers. *FIEP Bulletin*, **52**, 77-81.

PRIVES, M.G., & Aleksina, L.A. (1978). Influence of various kinds of sport on the skeletal growth in sportsmen. *Arkhiv Anatomii Gistologii*, **74**, 5-15.

RARICK, G.L. (1974). Exercise and growth. In W.R. Johnson & E.R. Buskirk (Eds.), *Science and medicine of exercise and sport*. New York: Harper & Row.

RJAZANOVA, Z.P. (1980). The skeleton of the hands of swimmers. *Arkhiv Anatomii Gistologii*, **78**, 10-14.

ROCHE, A.F. (1979). Secular trends in stature, weight, and maturation. *Monographs of the Society for Research in Child Development*, **44**, 3-27.

ROSS, J.G., Dotson, C.O., & Gilbert, G.G. (1985). Are kids getting appropriate activity? *Journal of Physical Education, Recreation & Dance*, **56**, 40-43.

SHEPHARD, R.J., Lavallee, H., Jequier, J.-C., Rajic, M., & LaBarre, R. (1980). Additional physical education in the primary school—A preliminary analysis of the

Trois Rivières regional experiment. In M. Ostyn (Ed.), *Kinanthropometry II.* Basel, Switzerland: Karger.

TANNER, J.M., & Whitehouse, R.H. (1962). Standards for subcutaneous fat in British children. *British Medical Journal, 1,* 446-450.

TANNER, J.M., & Whitehouse, R.H. (1975). Revised standards for triceps and subscapular skinfolds in British children. *Archives of Disease in Childhood, 50,* 142-145.

TRUSSELL, J. (1980). Statistical flaws in evidence for the Frisch hypothesis that fatness triggers menarche. *Human Biology, 52,* 711-720.

U.S. Department of Health and Human Services. (1980). *Promoting health/preventing disease: Objectives for the nation.* Washington, DC: Government Printing Office.

VERSCHUUR, R., Kemper, H.C.G., & Besseling, C.W.M. (1984). Habitual physical activity and health in 13- and 14-year-old teenagers. In J. Ilmarinen & I. Valmaki (Eds.), *Children in sport.* Berlin: Springer Verlag.

WARREN, M.P. (1980). The effects of exercise on pubertal progression and reproductive function in girls. *Journal of Clinical Endocrinology and Metabolism, 51,* 1150-1156.

WYZNIKIEWICZ-KOP, Z., & Kobuszewska, R. (1980). The effect of three years of differentiated training in girls aged twelve to fourteen years. Unpublished manuscript, Academy of Physical Education, Gdansk, Poland.

Weight Control Through Exercise and Diet for Children and Young Athletes

Melvin H. Williams
Old Dominion University

The late 1970s and early 1980s evidenced a renewed interest in the wellness movement with many adults adopting lifestyle changes in attempts to look and feel better, and perhaps to prolong life by preventing the early onset of several chronic diseases currently afflicting industrialized societies. A major health component of the wellness movement is maintenance of proper body weight, for excess body fat has been associated with increased mortality rates. For example, Clarke (1975) cites reports that the mortality rates were 79% for markedly overweight men and 42% for moderately overweight men, both being above-standard risk groups. Comparable figures were presented for overweight women. Weinhaus (1969) reports that for each 5 pounds above ideal weight, life expectancy is reduced by about 1 year.

A major reason for the increased mortality rate with obesity is its relationship to a number of diseases. Simonson (1982) reports that obesity is associated with at least 26 known medical conditions that could account collectively for 15 to 20% of the mortality rate. Obesity has been statistically related to kidney disease, cirrhosis of the liver, arthritis, diabetes, and coronary heart disease. Obesity is related to two of the primary risk factors of coronary heart disease, namely high levels of serum cholesterol and hypertension (Simonson, 1982). Langford (1982) notes that although the correlation between body weight and blood pressure is low ($r = .20-.30$), it is very consistent. Moreover, Hubert, Feinleib, and McNamara (1983) noted that obesity is now recognized as an independent risk factor for coronary heart disease. Indeed, a recent report from a National Institute of Health panel termed obesity a killer disease that deserves to be treated as seriously as any other illness (Cimons, 1985).

Although the prevailing medical opinion suggests that obesity is a major health problem for adults, a modified viewpoint has been advanced by several investigators. For example, Dietz (1983) noted that obesity is often referred to as a disease, but the point at which excessive fatness becomes pathologic is a subject of considerable debate. Wooley and Wooley (1984) support Dietz, indicating that the fundamental assumption that to become thinner is to become healthier is now the focus of increasing skepticism. Their review of the literature suggests that mild to moderate obesity does not appear to constitute a significant health risk for adult females, and possibly not even for adult males. They also note that the risk of early death increases only at the extremes of overweight.

Wellness has been a concern for young children and adolescents as well. Several major studies (Gilliam, Katch, Thorland, & Weltman, 1977; Lauer, Conner, & Leaverton, 1975; Spahn et al., 1982; Wilmore & McNamara, 1974) have reported the prevalence of a number of coronary heart disease risk factors in children, including elevated blood lipids, hypertension, and cigarette smoking.

As with adults, body weight control is also an important health concern for children. Although coronary heart disease per se is not very prevalent in children, the overall risk factor profile associated with its development is more pronounced in juvenile obesity (Czinner, Tichy, & Barta, 1983; Popa et al., 1984; Spahn et al., 1982). Several studies (Aristimuno, Foster, Voors, Srinivasan, & Berenson, 1984; Buzina et al., 1982; Epstein, Wing, Kuller, & Becker, 1983) have reported significant relationships between body weight and blood pressure, with obese children generally having higher systolic blood pressure. Aristimuno et al. (1984) also noted that very obese children also have significantly elevated diastolic blood pressure. Dietz (1983) concluded that obesity is the leading cause of pediatric hypertension. Increases in body fat are also generally associated with unfavorable serum lipid profiles in children (Buzina et al., 1982; Czinner et al., 1983; Epstein, Wing, et al., 1983; Gilliam, Thorland, & Sady, 1978; Tokunaga et al. 1982).

Most medical researchers believe that obese children have a risk profile favoring the development of coronary heart disease, but other investigators disagree. Mallick (1983) reviewed a number of studies in this area and reported that they had methodological flaws. She concluded that obesity is not necessarily related to an increased incidence of health problems, particularly hypertension. Research by Stallones, Mueller, and Christensen (1982) supports this latter aspect, for they found that fatness was not significantly related to blood pressure after body weight was factored in their regression equation. Brook (1983) also concluded that it is hard to find good evidence that obese children are more prone to disease than their lean peers. Although a number of medical risk factors are associated with obesity in childhood, the actual chronic medical diseases are not very prevalent at this age level.

Brownell (1984b) and Dietz (1983), two principal investigators of childhood obesity, believe that the primary risks of childhood obesity are social and psychological rather than medical. Since personality development occurs primarily in childhood and adolescence, excess body fat may contribute to emotional problems more so during this time than with adult-onset obesity (Mayer, 1972). For example, the Nutrition Committee of the Canadian Paediatric Society (1983) notes that obesity interferes with the development of a satisfying self-image and social status, which impairs normal psychological development. Obese children are often rejected by their peers, superiors, and even parents, resulting in a negative self-image, low self-esteem and even serious psychological illness. Mayer (1975b) has reported that the results of psychological testing in obese children reveals a profile similar to other types of children who suffer prejudice and discrimination. Shestowsky (1983) summarized the literature and reported that obese adolescent females were socially isolated, withdrawn individuals with feelings of alienation.

The time of onset of obesity may have some impact upon psychological problems. Shestowsky (1983), studying obese girls, reported that ego-identity problems were prevalent in puberty-onset obesity, but the ego identity scores in those adolescents who had childhood-onset obesity did not differ from those of normal-weight adolescent girls.

A contributing factor to the development of psychological problems may be the effect of excess fat on fitness and athletic performance. A number of studies (Beunen et al., 1983; Riendeau, 1958; Saris, Binkhorst, Cramwinckel, Van Waesberghe, & van der Veen-Hezemans, 1980) have revealed that increasing levels of body fatness are associated with poorer levels of motor fitness and performance. If the obese child is unsuccessful in play activities, he or she will probably not participate. A vicious cycle may be created, the withdrawal symptoms and absence of the socializing aspect of play contributing to improper psychological development at a critical stage in life and further alienating the child from play.

Although the prevailing opinion among psychologists is that obesity leads to an increased incidence of psychological disorders in children, particularly adolescent girls, some psychologists disagree. Mahoney and Klykylo (1983) state that the common belief of clinicians that obese children are more disturbed than their normal weight counterparts is difficult to prove statistically.

If indeed obesity does contribute to medical and psychological problems in children and adolescents, then industrialized countries appear to have a significant health problem. In the United States, Richmond, Blyler, and Linscheid (1983) estimate that 10 to 25% of grade-school children and 15% of adolescents are obese, while Brownell (1984b) notes that approximately 25% of American children are obese. Estimates in Canada are 5 to 20% (Nutrition Committee, Canadian Paediatric Society, 1983), in England approximately 2 to 10% (Stark, Atkins, Wolff, & Douglas, 1981), in Spain 10 to 15% (Sarria, 1983), and in Poland 23% of the boys (Charzewska & Figurska, 1983). There appears to be a progressive increase in the percentage of children classified as obese as they go from childhood to adolescence in Australia (Kelly, Sullivan, Bartsch, Gracey, & Ridout, 1984) and England (Stark et al., 1981).

The percentage of children being classified as obese also appears to be on the rise, as revealed by the recent National Children and Youth Fitness Study. Pate, Ross, Dotson, and Gilbert (1985) recently noted that American children have become fatter since the mid-1960s. Similar trends have been noted in England and Scotland (Rona & Chinn, 1984) and Singapore (Ho, Chay, Yie, Tay, & Wong, 1983).

Winick (1975) has noted that the kind of obesity developed at this time of life is particularly dangerous, for it may sentence the child to a lifetime of obesity. Hence, a prevention or treatment program for obesity would appear to be an important component of a total wellness program for youth. Seefeldt (1984) has noted that the general social environment for changing the daily living patterns of people, including children, has never been better. He also notes that schools must accept the challenge of the "Healthy People" report by the United States Government, which calls for the reduction of obesity levels in children.

DETERMINATION OF OBESITY IN CHILDREN

What is obesity? By medical definition it is simply an accumulation of an abnormal amount of fat in the body (Thomas, 1977). However, Brook (1978) has noted that obesity is indefinable because it is simply one end of the normal spectrum of body fatness in any given population. Garn, Clark, and Guire (1975) support this viewpoint, noting that we know little of childhood obesity including its very measurement and definition. Furthermore, a meeting of national experts (Committee on Nutrition of the Mother and Preschool Child, 1978) revealed a lack of unanimity regarding the definition and classification of obesity. Although the report noted that obesity in its broadest sense is a clinical presentation characterized by excessive fatness, there appears to be no consensus as to what constitutes excessive fatness or how this adiposity is to be measured.

Perusal of the literature supports this viewpoint. The two most common definitions of obesity in studies involving childhood obesity involve height-weight relationships and fat skinfold values. For height and weight, one of the more commonly used classifications of obesity is a body weight value greater than 120% of the standard weight for height, age, and sex (Ho et al., 1983; Richmond et al., 1983; Stark et al., 1981; Tokunaga et al., 1982). However, other investigators have suggested values of 115% (Epstein, Koeske, Zidansek, & Wing, 1983) and 130% (Laven, 1982). Bray (1984) has noted the use of a body mass index, such as weight in kilograms divided by height in meters squared, as a useful tool for classifying obesity in adults. However, Roche (1984) suggests these types of indices are of doubtful value with children. Triceps skinfold thickness values to classify obesity or unacceptable body fatness levels in children have also varied in different surveys or studies, ranging from the 75th percentile (Ross, Dotson, Gilberg, & Katz, 1985b), to the 85th (Dietz & Gortmaker, 1984) and even the 95th (Epstein, Koeske, et al., 1983). For those who use this technique, the best available data appears to have been collected in the recent National Children and Youth Fitness Study (Ross et al., 1985a). These data include triceps as well as the sum of triceps and subscapular skinfolds for boys and girls, separately, ages 10 to 18.

Skinfold values for younger children may be found in the *AAHPERD Health Related Physical Fitness Test Manual* (American Alliance for Health, Physical Education, Recreation and Dance, 1980). Body fat percentages are also being used to classify obesity, principally in adolescents. Ziegler (1982) suggests that adolescent boys should be about 10 to 15% body fat, while girls should be about 20 to 22% fat. Huenemann, Hampton, Behnke, Schapiro, and Mitchell (1974) classified obesity in adolescents as greater than 20% body fat in boys and 25% in girls. It should be noted that if underwater weighing techniques are utilized to determine body fat percentages, investigators should be aware that the standardized equations used with this technique may not be appropriate for children and may need further research (Lohman, 1982, 1984; Wilmore, 1983).

ETIOLOGY OF CHILDHOOD OBESITY

The etiology of childhood obesity is complex. The Committee on Nutrition of the Mother and Preschool Child (1978) noted that the obese state has no unique etiology; it is highly varied as to the age of onset, general health, endocrine and metabolic status, and innumerable psychosocial and behavioral concomitants. The current theory proposes multicausality involving the interaction of endogenous and exogenous variables. Endogenous factors include genetics, neuroendocrine imbalances, and metabolic disturbances whereas exogenous factors involve socioeconomic status, cultural background, nutrition, physical activity, and emotional states. To highlight this multicausal theory, Hirsch and Liebel (1984) note that the demonstration of a simple enzymatic effect or cellular defect, or of a particular behavioral or psychologic observation found in the obese, cannot be considered a sufficient description of the pathogenesis of obesity.

Heredity has been regarded as a contributing factor in the development of childhood obesity. Mayer (1975b) has noted that certain body types are associated with obesity, indicating a genetic component. He reported that if neither parent is obese, there is only a 7% chance of the child being obese. The percentage rises to 40 if one parent is obese and 80 if both are. Brook (1978) calculated that 80% of the variance in fatness in children is accounted for by genetic factors, but the actual proportion varies with age, sex, race, and other variables. This general viewpoint is modified somewhat by the Nutrition Committee of the Canadian Paediatric Society (1983), who report that the results from studies of twins and of families suggest it is apparent that while obesity is hereditary, the degree of heritability is not known. According to Knittle, Timmers, Ginsberg-Fellner, Brown, and Katz (1978) and Van Itallie (1984), no genetic marker for obesity has been found in humans. Nevertheless, there is strong support for the conclusion that obesity is a familial disorder, which may be related to an inherited tendency toward obesity coupled with faulty dietary habits in the family (Committee on Nutrition of the Mother and Preschool Child, 1979; Laron, Ben-Dan, Shrem, Dickerman, & Lilos, 1978; Richmond et al., 1983).

Stunkard (1984) discussed a new theory for obesity in adults, suggesting that it is the result of regulated homeostatic processes that maintain body fat at an elevated level. This may involve a number of physiological mechanisms which, if disturbed, could lead to weight gain. These might include brown adipose tissue activity, sodium and potassium ATPase activity, substrate cycling, lipoprotein lipase activity, and the glycerol phosphate shuttle mechanism (McMinn, 1984). Much of the theory centers upon disturbances in thermogenesis from brown adipose tissue, theorizing a defective thermogenic response to food intake or strict dieting which could lead to weight gain (Bray, 1983; Jequier, 1983; Mayer, 1983). However, Ashwell (1983) has reported that the evidence is still very scant for thermogenesis, let alone brown adipose tissue, having an important role in the etiology of obesity.

It should be noted there are some definite pathological endogenous causes of obesity, such as lesions in the hypothalamus and endocrine disorders like Cushing's syndrome, Prader-Willi syndrome, and insulinoma (Richmond et al., 1983). However, these appear to afflict only a very small percentage of children (Dietz, 1983).

Although there are endogenous causes of obesity in children, Richmond et al. (1983) note that the most common type of obesity is exogenous. Their review suggests that improper diet and inadequate physical activity are the key exogenous factors. They note that obese children can be identified early by their characteristic eating and physical activity patterns. Brownell (1984a) also notes that childhood is a time when most persons develop and solidify eating and activity patterns.

Does overeating contribute to the development of obesity in children? Brownell (1984b) suggests that the supermarket diet of today with its high sugar and fat content could be a major factor in obesity. However, in a major study of 1,000 teenagers over a 4-year period, Huenemann et al. (1974) obtained 7-day records of the girls' dietary intake and concluded that obese adolescents took in fewer calories per unit of body weight than nonobese adolescents. On the other hand, the Nutrition Committee of the Canadian Paediatric Society (1983) criticized the design of most studies that have reported that the obese child does not eat more than the nonobese, for many of these studies were not done during periods of weight gain. In one of the few studies employing direct observation techniques in the home and at school, Waxman and Stunkard (1980) concluded that obese boys in general eat more than their nonobese brothers, and much more than their nonobese peers. They also eat more rapidly. The results of this study provide some of the best available evidence that excess caloric intake is a contributing factor to obesity in children.

Is physical inactivity a cause of childhood obesity? Some studies suggest that it is. Huenemann et al. (1974) studied 1,000 teenagers for 4 years and noted that, in general, the obese subjects had a very low level of physical activity. Parizkova (1972) subdivided a large group of boys into categories based upon levels of physical activity and reported that at all ages the most active had the lower amounts of absolute body fat. Shestowsky (1983), summarizing the literature, concluded that obese adolescent girls were grossly inactive. Other circumstantial evidence, such as an increased incidence of obesity in winter compared to summer, suggests that physical inactivity may contribute to the development of childhood obesity (Dietz & Gortmaker, 1984).

However, other research does not support this viewpoint. In a well-controlled study involving direct observation of physical activity patterns at home and in school, Waxman and Stunkard (1980) noted that although the obese boys were slightly less active outside the home, they were equally active in school. Moreover, they concluded that the obese children actually expended more calories than the nonobese in physical activity because it cost them more calories to move their bodies.

Brownell (1984a) indicates that currently there is confusion on the issue of energy expenditure of obese as compared to lean children. Vasselli, Cleary, and Van Itallie (1983) also note that whether physical inactivity in general precedes or follows the development of obesity is not clear. In the most recent thorough evaluation, Dotson and Ross (1985) note that the relationship between physical activity and body fatness is complex and even paradoxical. For example, in comparing various subgroup ranges, students in the acceptable or below-average ranges of skinfold thicknesses report spending greater amounts of time and energy in physical activity than students in the optimal range. Dotson and Ross note a possible interpretation of this paradox may be that the students think physical activity alone is sufficient for regulation of body composition. They conclude that other factors besides physical activity patterns, particularly diet, are important in determining body composition.

Stern (1984) recently addressed the question, "Is obesity a disease of inactivity?" His response was "definitely maybe." Stern noted that for those who are considerably less active than lean individuals, for those with low calorie requirements, and for those who respond to a modest increase in physical activity by decreasing food intake, obesity can be considered a disease of physical inactivity.

ONSET AND PERSISTENCE OF CHILDHOOD OBESITY

The actual deposition of fat in the human body may occur in two ways. Hirsh (1972) has noted that obesity is achieved through an increase in both number and fat content of adipose cells. Winick (1974), reviewing a 1973 conference on childhood obesity, also noted that the fat in the adipose tissue may be packaged in a large number of small cells (hyperplastic obesity), or in a smaller number of large cells (hypertrophic obesity).

Brook (1983) has indicated there is no evidence to suggest that the fat cell of an obese individual is inherently different from that of a normal-weight individual. Obese children simply have, on the average, more and larger fat cells than nonobese children at all age levels studied (Knittle, 1975). The Committee on Nutrition of the Mother and Preschool Child (1978) reports that obese children at age 2 obtain levels of fat cells comparable in size to those of nonobese adults. Subsequently, increases in fat stores occur almost exclusively by increases in fat cell number. Brook (1983) and Vasselli et al. (1983) note that fat cell hypertrophy may stimulate hyperplasia, which may occur at this time of life when the fat cells reach their maximum size. Knittle et al. (1979) reported that by age 11 the mean number of fat cells in obese children exceeded that of nonobese adults. Doyard, Chaussain, and Job (1978) noted that hypercellularity is a striking feature of obesity beginning in childhood; indeed, Bonnett, Duckerts, and Heuskin (1976) reported that 80% of overweight children are of the hyperplastic type. In contrast, nonobese children show little growth in adipose tissue mass from age 2 until 10 to 12 years, at which time cell size and number increase to adult levels.

There appear to be several critical periods during childhood when the rate of adipose tissue increase may be accelerated. Although Olson (1984) indicates that the concept of hyperplasia in the etiology of obesity has been overemphasized, he does note that the body has the ability to add new adipocytes but is unable to decrease existing ones. Brownell (1984b) notes, however, that cell numbers can be reduced in individuals who lose a great deal of weight.

Perusal of the literature reveals a number of different critical periods including, chronologically, the last trimester of pregnancy (Hirsch, 1975), the first 2 to 3 years of life (Heald, 1972, 1975; Hirsch, 1975; Knittle, 1975; Knittle et al., 1979), the beginning of school at about age 6 (Heald, 1975; Rolland-Cachera et al., 1984; Van Itallie & Hashim, 1970), preadolescence (Doyard et al., 1978; Knittle, 1975), and adolescence (Bonnet, 1978; Heald, 1975; Hirsch, 1972, 1975; Knittle, 1975; Van Itallie & Hashim, 1970). This appears to span the whole of childhood, reinforcing the conclusion that the obese state has no unique etiology relative to age of onset (Committee on Nutrition of the Mother and Preschool Child, 1978).

How persistent is childhood-onset obesity? Does an early-onset obesity predispose the child to a lifetime of excess adiposity? Some feel there is no convincing evidence that the obese child becomes an obese adult (Committee on Nutrition of the Mother and Preschool Child, 1978) while others feel that fat hypercellularity acquired during childhood may have lifelong duration (Doyard et al., 1978). The answer to this question may depend upon the degree to which obesity persists throughout childhood.

First, does early nutrition predispose to obesity? Vobecky, Vobecky, Shapcott, and Demers (1983) believe not. They studied the dietary intake of 170 infants over a 36-month period and report that the results do not support the hypothesis that overfeeding in early infancy is a major cause of obesity in later life. Wolman (1984) studied 262 infants for 4 years and report that neither breast-feeding itself nor its duration was related to the prevalence of obesity. Nor did the time of introduction of solid foods influence the prevalence of obesity.

Does obesity during infancy persist into later childhood and adulthood? Some evidence suggests it does. Richmond et al. (1983) suggests that 45% of adult obesity cases actually begin in infancy, primarily due to eating and activity patterns. Charney, Goodman, and McBride (1976) report that the risk of an obese infant becoming an obese adult is 36%. They note that 36% of those infants who exceeded the 90th percentile of weight for height in the first 6 months of life were overweight as adults, compared to only 14% of the average and light-weight infants. However, two major reviews support generally an opposing point of view. The Committee on Nutrition of the Mother and Preschool Child (1978) note that the available data do not support the hypothesis that fat infants become fat children, although there may be a need to distinguish between moderate and extreme obesity. The Nutrition Committee of the Canadian Paediatric Society (1983) conclude the current evidence suggests that fat infants become normal weight children, but that many fat children and adolescents were fat infants. Probably the best response to this issue is offered by Hovels, Makosch, and Bergmann (1982), who note that although it has not been proven that obese infants become obese adults, obesity in infancy should not be disregarded.

Does obesity in later childhood and adolescence persist into adulthood? Although the concept of the persistence of obesity from infancy to adulthood is controversial, there is a greater unanimity of opinion relative to its persistence from later childhood and adolescence into adulthood. Rolland-Cachera et al. (1984) report that after age 6 the prediction of obesity in later years increases. Aristimuno et al. (1984) studied 2,230 children over a 5-year period and found a strong tendency for tracking relative to body fat, that is, the obese and very obese tend to remain that way. The Nutrition Committee of the Canadian Paediatric Society (1983) also note a strong relationship between obesity in late preschool years and adolescence. Obesity also tends to persist throughout the adolescent years. Huenemann et al. (1974) note that all but 2% of those who were obese in grade 12 were also obese in grade 9. However, there may be some gender differences here. Ross, Dotson, Gilbert, and Katz (1985a), using data from the National Children and Youth Fitness Study, found that boys become relatively more lean at puberty from age 13 through age 15 to 16 and then maintain a constant level through age 17 to 18. This may support previous remarks by Mayer (1975b) who, based upon his experience, noted that the obesity developing just before the pubertal growth spurt in boys may be benign and self-correcting. Ross et al. (1985a) note that girls, however, increase their body fatness at a constant rate from age 10 to 16 and then taper off in the rate of fat gain. These findings may be related to the report by Abraham and Nordsieck (1960) that 15% of obese men and 75% of obese women had childhood antecedents of obesity.

The later into adolescence the individual remains obese, the greater the persistence of obesity into adulthood. Stark et al. (1981) report that while 40% of those who were overweight at age 11 were still overweight at age 26, the percentage increased to 50 if they were still overweight at age 14. Kelly et al. (1984), in an 11-year study, report that 40% of those who were obese between the ages of 9 and 14 were still obese in young adult life. Abraham and Nordsieck (1960) report that the risk of an obese adolescent becoming an obese adult is 63 to 72%. These general findings have been supported by Hovels et al. (1982) and the Nutrition Committee of the Canadian Paediatric Society (1983).

PREVENTION AND TREATMENT OF CHILDHOOD OBESITY

The ideal way to confront the problem of childhood obesity is through prevention. Experts note the prognosis for childhood obesity is poor when it is fully developed, so it makes sense to give more attention to preventive measures such as proper dietary and exercise education programs (Dietz, 1983; Knittle & Ginsberg-Fellner, 1975; Parizkova, 1982; Spahn et al., 1982; Van Itallie, 1984).

When should a prevention program be initiated? As discussed previously, there may be certain critical time periods in the child's development when the onset of obesity is more likely to occur. Although Brook (1978) notes that we still need to identify these preventive periods, that is, when preventive action is likely to be effective, other investigators have offered some general recommendations. Knittle (1975) notes that both human and animal studies support the hypothesis that intervention must be instituted prior to the development of the hypercellular state. Relative to this point, Simic (1983) suggests that the prevention of obesity should begin in the intrauterine stage, as overeating by pregnant women may result in heavier babies, which he notes will more likely become obese. Others (Costom & Shore, 1983; Knittle, 1975; Spahn et al., 1982;

Weil, 1975) recommend that dietary therapy be initiated in infancy if the child begins to exceed the normal weight/height ratio. The Nutrition Committee of the Canadian Paediatric Society (1983), Hovels et al. (1982), and Knittle (1975) theorize that prevention before the age of 6 or 7 is desirable, but unfortunately there are no data from intervention studies at this age level. Dietz (1983) and Parizkova (1982) note that preventive programs prior to the onset of puberty and adolescence are necessary, while Stark et al. (1981) suggest that adolescence, ages 11 to 20, may be a critical period for trying to prevent obesity in adulthood.

The previous discussion relative to critical time periods for the development of childhood obesity reveals that it could occur at any time. The discussion immediately above also suggests that preventive programs may be initiated at any time. In general, there is very little difference between a preventive program and a treatment program for obesity relative to dietary and exercise behaviors. The major focus of the discussion below will center upon treatment programs but the same approach, with some possible modifications, would also be appropriate for prevention. Many authorities in the field of obesity indicate that treatment is difficult and very often ineffective (Nutrition Committee, Canadian Paediatric Society, 1983; Van Itallie, 1984; Wooley & Wooley, 1984). Indeed, Brownell (1984b) has noted that the cure rate for obesity, that is, to reduce to the ideal weight and maintain it for 5 years, is lower than the cure rate for cancer.

With adults, dozens of methods have been utilized in attempts to reduce body fat or body weight, including anorectic drugs to decrease the appetite, stimulant drugs or hormones to increase the metabolism, drugs or a teflon-like coating to decrease absorption of food from the intestine, diuretics, bulking agents, or balloons in the stomach to create a sensation of fullness, wrapping the stomach in a plastic mesh to prevent expansion, wiring the jaw shut, hypnosis, acupuncture, and surgical techniques such as stapling the stomach, intestinal bypass surgery, and excision or suction removal of subcutaneous adipose tissue (Friedman, Kindy, & Reinke, 1982; National Dairy Council, 1978; Simonson, 1982). Although the surgical techniques are usually a last resort, many adults have used the various drugs to treat obesity. However, Grollman (1975) indicates that drug therapy is contraindicated under age 12 and has not yet been proven safe or effective for older children. On the other hand, Barta et al. (1982) report that caffeine, in a dose of 4 mg/kg, could improve exercise capacity in children and they suggest it might be used at the beginning of a training program to lose weight.

Unfortunately, many of the techniques noted above may have serious side effects, and some are still in the experimental stage, with unknown long-term effects. (See the National Dairy Council, 1978, for some of the associated problems.) Moreover, the majority of individuals who use these techniques may regain the lost body weight once the treatment is stopped and the human energy balance equation again becomes positive.

The key feature of any treatment program for childhood obesity is the need for lifestyle change (Nutrition Committee, Canadian Paediatric Society, 1983). In order to implement such a change, the comprehensive weight reduction program recommended for most individuals with excess body fat and uncomplicated obesity involves three main components:

1. A dietary regimen stressing balanced nutrition, but with reduced caloric intake;
2. An aerobics exercise program to increase caloric expenditure;
3. A behavior modification program to facilitate the implementation of the first two components.

This approach has been recommended by professional organizations such as the American Dietetic Association (1980), the American College of Sports Medicine (1983), and other authorities in the area of childhood obesity (Brownell, Kelman, & Stunkard, 1983; Grollman, 1975; Knittle & Ginsberg-Fellner, 1975; McMinn, 1984). Recent experimental studies with adults (Weltman, Tran, Schurrer, & Melcher, 1983) and children (Brownell & Kaye, 1982) have also supported such an approach, as have literature reviews by Dahlkoetter, Callahan, and Linton (1979) and Thompson, Jarvie, Lahey, and Cureton (1982). Another important component of such a program, which may be part of the behavioral modification component, is to provide social and psychological support to the child (Brownell et al., 1983; Mayer, 1975a, 1975b).

To reemphasize a point, Steffer (1982) notes that the two basic precepts of therapy—eat less and exercise more—are not as simple as they appear when applied to the treatment of clinical obesity, which he notes is a complex medical disorder. Although the cause of excess body fat is an excessive energy intake in comparison to energy expenditure, the mechanisms that regulate food intake and energy expenditure are complex and may not operate properly in some individuals, which may lead to an obesity resistive to treatment. However, even with hereditary or genetic predispositions, these mechanisms may be effective in reducing excess body fat. As Mayer (1968) has noted, genes may make one susceptible to obesity, but overeating and underexercise have to accompany it. The constitutional factors operating in the predisposition to obesity do not detract from recommending this program.

There may be some precautions in advising a weight reduction program for children. Since this is a period of anabolism, several authorities caution that severely restricting calories at this time may restrict proper growth and development (Heald, 1975; Mayer, 1975a). This may be a particular problem with adolescents, the majority of whom undertake weight control without direct medical supervision (Mallick, 1983). For adults, the recommended amount of weight loss during unsupervised programs is about 2 pounds per week. However, Mann (1977) suggests that the loss of 1 to 2 pounds per week may be too much for youngsters. He notes that such weight losses will compromise growth. He does suggest that weight losses below age 16 should be accomplished primarily by exercise, not diet. Pena, Barta, Regoly-Merei, and Tichy (1980) support this concept, noting that although children can lose weight by dieting, the losses may be in the form of lean body mass and may interfere with growth and development. They recommend a mild restriction of caloric intake combined with an exercise program. With a diet balanced in nutrients combined with an aerobic exercise program, a loss of 1 pound per week would appear to be reasonable for children who have excess fat (Gregg, 1970); however, medical advice should be obtained.

There are a number of precautions one should note before implementing a weight reduction program. First is the need to see a physician if there are any health concerns associated with the excess body weight. The physician may check for endocrine imbalances or metabolic abnormalities and analyze dietary and physical activity habits, recommending appropriate therapy. If a commercial weight loss center is available, check to see that it has a physician available or is recommended by local medical or dietetic groups.

Dieting

A proper diet is an important component of a weight reduction program for all individuals. Dietz (1983) indicates it is the cornerstone of the program for young children, and Knittle's (1975) research data clearly indicates that with childhood obesity, dietary modifications should be implemented prior to age 6, or age 2 in some cases, if a lifelong history of obesity is to be avoided. Two national medical groups also recently published their opinions on healthy diets for children with the intent of helping to establish proper eating habits early in life and possibly helping to prevent atherosclerotic development later in life, as well as preventing obesity in childhood (American Heart Association, 1983; Committee on Nutrition, American Academy of Pediatrics, 1983). In general the recommendations favored caloric control for proper weight and a moderate reduction of cholesterol, saturated fat, simple sugar, and sodium intake. Complex carbohydrates were stressed as important components of the diet.

Four general principles provide the basis for a successful diet:

1. It should be low in calories and yet supply all nutrients essential to normal body functions.
2. It should contain foods that appeal to the taste and help to prevent hunger sensations between meals.
3. It should accommodate itself to the current lifestyle by being easily obtainable either at home or elsewhere.
4. It should be a lifelong diet and one that will satisfy the above three principles once the desired weight is attained.

The first principle above will provide the caloric deficit for the weight loss, but in order for the diet to be lifelong it has to be agreeable to each individual's taste and lifestyle.

Severe calorie-restricted diets are not suitable for most obese children. Research with obese adults (Bray, 1983) suggests that such diets may lead to a decrease in the basal metabolic rate and thus be counterproductive, although no research has been uncovered relative to this effect in obese children. For infants, Richmond et al. (1983) recommends that the weight be maintained until the child grows into the proper weight/height channel. With young children they recommend an initial deficit of about 250 to 500 calories but not below the lower limits of the RDA. For mildly to moderately obese adolescents Dietz (1983) recommends a deficit of 1/3 of the usual intake, but with very obese adolescents notes that a medically supervised protein-modified fast (700 to 1000 cal; 1.5 g protein/kg) could be utilized.

Some recent research with dieting illustrates that it may be effective in some children. Scavo, Giovannini, Sellini, and Fierro (1978) induced weight loss through dieting alone in 431 children over a 6- to 9-month period. Over 61% showed a significant reduction, and nearly 43% maintained the weight loss for 18 to 24 months following the treatment phase. However, the older children (age 13 to 15) were more successful than the younger ones in maintaining the weight loss. A study of very obese children on a low-calorie (500 to 700 cal) but high-protein diet demonstrated a weight loss of 20 to 25% over 5 months. Some 36% of the weight loss in the first 5 weeks was from lean body mass, but this volume decreased to only 10% over the next 4 months and did not appear to hamper linear growth (Brown, Klish, Hollander, Campbell, & Forbes, 1983). Although diet is an essential component of a weight reduction program, it is more effective if combined with exercise.

Exercise

As noted previously, lack of physical activity may be an important variable affecting obesity. Ten years ago Mayer (1975b) termed it the most important variable, and some recent data support this viewpoint. For example, the Nutrition Committee of the Canadian Paediatric Society (1983) reports that the average preschool child in North America watches 30 to 54 hours of television per week. Data from the National Children and Youth Fitness Study reveal that only about half of American children in grades 5 to 12 get enough physical activity to maintain an effective cardiovascular system (Ross, Dotson, & Gilbert, 1985). This may also mean they are physically inactive relative to proper weight control. A review of the previous discussion relative to the etiology of obesity provides strong, although not universal, support for the role of physical inactivity.

A proper aerobic exercise program is an effective adjunct to dieting in the treatment of obesity. Relative to losing weight, the most important benefit from such a program is the increased metabolic rate which expends more calories. Exercise also stimulates hormonal secretions that help with the use of fat stores as energy sources. These same hormonal adjustments, plus an increased body temperature, will lead to an elevated basal metabolism during the recovery period. Exercise may also suppress the appetite (Brownell, 1984b; Vasselli et al., 1983). It is also believed that exercise helps prevent the loss of protein and the decrease in metabolic rate resulting from caloric restriction (Brownell, 1984b; McMinn, 1984; Vasselli et al., 1983), but Bjorntorp (1983) notes that these effects are not totally clear at present.

Several major reviews with adults illustrate that exercise can be effective in reducing excess body fat. Epstein and Wing (1980) conducted a meta-analysis of the available research and concluded that the effects of exercise on weight were reliable and directly related to energy expenditure. Persons who exercise lose more weight than those who do not, and thin individuals lose less weight than heavier ones. Wilmore (1983) concluded that exercise training appears to result in moderate losses in total body weight, moderate to large losses in body fat, and small to moderate gains in lean body mass.

There appear to be limits to the effects of exercise training with the very obese. Pollock, Wilmore, and Fox (1984) note that the response to physical training programs seems to be a function of the degree of obesity at the start of the program. In general, the most obese appear to receive less benefits than those who are only mildly obese. Since, as these authors note, children adapt to aerobic training about the same as adults, this problem may exist with very obese children as well. Nevertheless, Bray (1983) notes that exercise is a good approach to treating obesity, particularly in children and adolescents, and should be the first line of treatment.

Unfortunately, obese children do not adhere well to exercise training programs even though they know that exercise is effective. This may be due to associated locomotor problems which complicate training (Hamborg, 1982) or to the fact that exercise in the obese imposes greater energy demands and is therefore more difficult to do, leading to an aversion to exercise (Brownell, 1984a; Parizkova, 1982).

These problems should be considered in developing an exercise program for the obese. The program should be designed to strengthen self-confidence, not to weaken it. It should be individualized, tailored to the needs and capabilities of each child so that he or she experiences success. An aerobic exercise program, following sound principles of intensity, duration, frequency, and progression, can easily be adapted to the individual. Also, as much as possible the exercise should be fun, enjoyable, and social in nature. Just as dieting to lose weight is more effective when combined with an exercise program, the converse is also true.

Behavior Modification

The third component of a comprehensive weight reduction program is behavior modification, a technique often used in psychological therapy to elicit desirable behavioral changes. The rationale underlying behavior modification is that many behavioral patterns are learned via stimulus-response conditioning in that a particular stimulus in one's environment will elicit a conditioned response. Since such responses are learned, they may also be unlearned. Relative to weight control, behavior modification is used primarily to control stimuli, eliminate cues and restructure attitudes that may lead to excessive eating or physical inactivity. Various motivational techniques are used to enhance compliance. In essence, behavior modification for weight control involves changing eating and exercise habits. Brownell (1984b) believes that behavior modification holds the most promise for long-term success and therefore should be a component of any program designed to last a lifetime.

A key factor in behavior modification for weight control in children is to provide social support from significant others in the child's environment. Mallick (1983) notes that one way to help cure obesity may be to develop a feeling of acceptance of the obese. Elimination of negative moralistic social pressures may help foster the development of self-confidence.

Parental involvement is essential. Parents should be educated in the basic principles of diet and exercise and, optimally, serve as role models for the child (Epstein et al., 1983b; Knittle & Ginsberg-Fellner, 1975). The type of parental involvement is also important; Brownell et al. (1983) found that when a comprehensive weight control program was given to children and their mothers separately, as compared to a group of children who were treated with their mothers or a group of children whose mothers were not involved, they lost more weight and a year later still had a significant weight loss while the latter two groups had gained weight.

A variety of behavior modification techniques are available. For more information the reader is referred to Mahoney and Mahoney (1970), Leitenberg (1976), Mahoney (1975), Dusek (1982), or Wilson (1980). Many medical clinics for weight loss, as well as groups such as Weight Watchers, use behavior modification techniques and may serve as sources of information.

School-Based Programs

The comprehensive approach to weight control has been utilized in a variety of settings, including obesity research clinics, university weight control centers, national medical clinics, and nonmedical groups such as Weight Watchers. One approach with children which has produced some degree of success is the camp program. A number of studies conducted with obese children have indicated that a 7- to 8-week camp experience designed for weight loss would lead to significant weight reduction and improvement in fitness (Krawczuk-Rybakowa & Urban, 1984; McKenzie, Buono, & Nelson, 1984; Parizkova, Vaneckova, & Vamberova, 1962; Sprynarova & Parizkova, 1965). However, Parizkova (1982) noted that these changes were usually only temporary; upon returning home, the children reverted to or even surpassed their former weight.

Brownell (1984b), a national authority on childhood obesity, noted that the school is one potentially powerful source of support for control of body weight, but it remains largely untapped. This concept was advanced previously by Mayer (1968), who was convinced that an effective program consisting of increased physical exercise, dietary education, and psychological support could be incorporated into the public school system.

Several early studies have shown that a comprehensive weight reduction program can be effective in a public school situation. Christakis, Sajecki, and Hillman (1966) studied the effect of a combined program of physical fitness and nutritional education upon the degree of obesity in 90 high school boys. An experimental and a control group were utilized over an 18-month period, and the results indicated that the program was very effective in reducing the obesity of those boys who had been grossly obese at the start. Seltzer and Mayer (1970) undertook a study whose purpose was to ascertain whether a program for obese youngsters could be successfully instituted in a large public school system. Special physical activity programs for the obese were conducted 5 days a week instead of the usual 2 days. No attempt was made to place the obese children on low-calorie diets, although nutritional information was discussed. The results indicated that the program was effective in reducing obesity. Mayer (1975a) notes that similar programs could and probably should be an integral part of public school systems at all levels.

More recent research also supports the value of these programs. Brownell and Kaye (1982) report that a school-based behavior modification, nutrition education, and physical activity program for obese children helped 95% of those involved to lose weight. The students lost an average of about 10 pounds—a 15.4% decrease in their percentage overweight—on the 10-week program. Ylitalo (1981) conducted a similar study stressing diet and exercise over a 2-year period, and reported that 50% of the schoolchildren in the exercise-diet group achieved normal weight or lost a significant amount of weight. Lansky and Brownell (1982), using a behavioral modification approach with diet and exercise, reported that 63% of the participating adolescents declined in percentage of overweight for weight/height ratios. Other examples of successful programs have been reported by Botvin, Cantlon, Carter, and Williams (1979), Lansky and Vance (1983), and Ruppenthal and Gibbs (1979).

It is time for the administrators of physical education programs in the public schools to devote increased attention to the specific physical needs of obese students. Some school systems already have well developed programs, but this is the exception rather than the rule. Over 10 years ago, Moody (1971) suggested that it is the responsibility of physical educators to develop a program for the obese student—possibly patterned after an organization such as Weight Watchers—with regular meetings, record-keeping, and provision of appropriate materials and advice. A similar suggestion is advanced by Ash Hayes (1984), chairman of the President's Council on Physical Fitness and Sports, who notes that obese children are disabled and should be identified and helped.

The objectives for promoting health and preventing disease in America, as released by the U.S. Dept. of Health and Human Services (1980), have important implications for persons involved in the education of children, particularly those of us in health and physical education. Seefeldt (1984) notes that the educational implications of attempting to change traditional patterns of nutrition and physical activity in youth, two of the general objectives in this report, suggest the school would be a logical place to start. Since proper weight control is an underlying objective of this governmental report, it is incumbent upon our profession to accept this challenge and adapt our programs to meet this objective.

Students themselves seem to want such a program. For example, Canning and Mayer (1968) studied the attitudes and knowledge of weight control in obese and normal-weight adolescent girls. They found that the obese girls had more awareness and interest in the issues of obesity and weight control, and more positive attitudes toward exercise, than did the normal-weight girls. Canning and Mayer suggest that the physical educator exploit these interests and attitudes to help the obese initiate and maintain an effective diet and exercise program. Huenemann et al. (1974) also pointed out that adolescents are very interested in their figure and the majority are willing to take the necessary steps to improve it. Collipp (1975) reported that, contrary to some expectations, well-designed school weight control programs were enthusiastically received by students and there were no reports of embarrassment or isolation from friends because of the program.

What are some of the key elements of such a program? First, a team approach should be used including health educators, physical educators, the school nurse, food service personnel, community resource personnel, and parents. Education of the parents appears to be critical in any behavior modification program for weight control, and their degree of involvement seems significantly related to the outcome (Lansky & Vance, 1983). Food service personnel may also contribute to the program by developing tasty, nutritious, low-calorie meals and advertising their nutrition quality (Fieldhouse, 1982).

Second, identify those children in need of treatment. The AAHPERD Health Related Fitness Test's body composition analysis could be useful here, as could standard weight/height tables. Knittle and Ginsberg-Fellner (1975) reflect the opinion of most investigators in this field when they note that early identification is very important. Unfortunately, as Little (1983) notes, health education is so limited in early school years that obesity prevention and management efforts seldom reach the child.

Third, the program should involve the trilogy of nutrition, exercise, and behavior modification as previously noted and recently described by Sartorius and Solberg (1984) for a large school system. Regular health and physical education classes could provide basic information important in preventing weight gain in normal-weight children. Emphasis would be placed upon after-school and weekend physical activity. Parents could be involved indirectly. For example, Coates, Jeffery, and Slinkard (1981) used an educational program to change the dietary and exercise habits of elementary schoolchildren and also to see if the changes would generalize to other family members. The result was a substantial change in the children's eating behavior and, as reported by parents, a favorable change in family eating habits as well. The changes persisted over a 4-month follow-up period. Children in need of treatment could be helped by individualized instruction, special classes, or a health club. Brownell (1984b) suggests that the children be screened for such special programs, however. This would eliminate anyone who is not motivated to succeed, for if the child fails to lose weight it may increase the psychological trauma he or she is already experiencing and may create the impression that he or she has a legacy of failure. Also, a negative attitude in one individual may become contagious and adversely affect the outcome for the whole group. One good screening approach is to use a pilot program for 2 weeks.

In summary, although this type of school-based program has been shown effective in reducing weight and degree of obesity in many children, the dropout rate is appreciable and the success rate only moderate. Moreover, there is a dire need for more long-range research to see if the results persist for several years. Collipp (1975) suggests we need a good prospective study that will follow children for 12 years. Nevertheless, the success rates that have been reported are substantial enough to warrant that such weight control programs be implemented and/or continued in our school systems.

WEIGHT LOSS FOR SPORTS COMPETITION

There are a number of sports in which a lower body weight may confer some biomechanical advantage, particularly those sports that would require additional strength or energy to move any extra body weight, such as gymnastics, ballet, and distance running. Thus, participants in these sports often attempt to lose excess body fat and are among the leanest of athletes. However, the most serious attempts at weight reduction for athletic competition occur in amateur wrestling. The wrestler assumes that if he can maintain his strength and endurance in a lower weight class, he may have a decided advantage in force and leverage over his opponent.

The recommended method for losing excess body weight for athletic competition involves a balanced low-calorie diet and exercise, so the principles and guidelines presented here relative to a safe and effective weight control program for children in general is also appropriate for young athletes. Most athletes use this approach to attain their optimal weight, including wrestlers during the initial stages of weight loss. However, wrestlers tend to lose most of their body weight in the day or two immediately preceding competition, primarily by starvation and dehydration—two techniques that have caused concern among sports medicine personnel.

The question as to whether starvation and dehydration affect the health of the mature wrestler has been debated for years. In general, however, these practices have been condemned by such medical groups as the Committee on the Medical Aspects of Sports of the American Medical Association (1967) and the American College of Sports Medicine (1976). Of major medical concern is the effect that starvation and dehydration techniques may have upon children who are still in the growth and development stages of life. Zambraski (1980) has noted that young wrestlers are at an age where nutritional needs are critical. Yet the perceived importance of "making weight" often outweighs the consideration of a balanced diet, adequate fluid intake, and sensible caloric requirements.

As mentioned earlier, achieving and maintaining a normal body weight during childhood is important for a variety of reasons. Indeed, Amundson (1973) noted that the child who is overfed or overweight suffers more damage to health than the young man or woman who is exercising hard to lose weight. The potential health problems are incurred when a youngster sets out to reach an unrealistically low body weight goal and then employs techniques such as starvation, dehydration, diuretics, and appetite suppressant drugs to accomplish his goal. Sharman (1982) has suggested that the urge to decrease body fat for athletic competition may create a conscious and voluntary pathological aversion to food and fatness. He noted that the degree of body wasting in some athletes may be so severe as to be diagnosed as anorexia nervosa; both sexes are at equal risk, including adolescent and even preadolescent males.

Warren (1984) has termed this condition *anorexia athletica*. Females may develop secondary amenorrhea (Ziegler, 1982). However, both Sharman (1982) and Smith (1982) point out that the emotional drive of wrestlers to make weight is usually only temporary and not a chronic deep-seated problem as seen in true anorexia nervosa. Therefore, the treatment prognosis is good. Clinical symptoms such as decreased testosterone levels return to normal after the season (Strauss, Lanese, & Malarkey, 1984). Nevertheless, coaches should be aware of the symptoms of anorexia nervosa and look for them if weight reduction is important to their sport (Smith, 1982). Chipman, Hagan, and Edlin (1983) note, however, that it is difficult to differentiate between the true anorexec and the normal athlete who is losing weight. They cite the case study of a 14-year-old boy who wanted to achieve an ideal body weight for distance running. Only after a thorough psychological evaluation revealed a disturbed body image and marked feelings of inadequacy was his case diagnosed as anorexia nervosa.

Prolonged starvation at critical periods will have a detrimental effect upon growth and development if the needs for protein, zinc, and other essential growth nutrients are not met. But little is known of the effects of short-term starvation and dehydration techniques as practiced by wrestlers. Over a decade ago, Mayer (1972) posed some interesting questions that have yet to be adequately researched. What is the effect of these weight reduction practices on growing and developing youngsters? Are there any pathological consequences of hyperketonemia and dehydration? What are the long-term effects on the liver and other organs of alternating total fasting and refeeding?

The American College of Sports Medicine (1976) recommends encouraging local health and sport organizations to systematically collect data on wrestlers' weight reduction practices and study the effects upon their growth and development. However, very little effort has been directed toward that recommendation (Sady, Thomson, Savage, & Petratis, 1982). One study by Freischlag (1984) followed a group of 104 high school wrestlers over a 2-year period, and compared several health factors with a group of 73 control subjects. Although the wrestlers seemed to have less energy, as documented by parents, neither illness nor emotional feelings appeared to be related to weight loss in this population. As with weight reduction programs for children in general, this area is in dire need of longitudinal research efforts.

REFERENCES

ABRAHAM, S., & Nordsieck, M. (1960). Relationship of excess weight in children and adults. *Public Health Reports, 75,* 263-273.

AMERICAN Alliance for Health, Physical Education, Recreation and Dance. (1980). *AAHPERD Health Related Physical Fitness Test Manual.* Reston, VA: Author.

AMERICAN College of Sports Medicine. (1983). Proper and improper weight loss programs. *Medicine and Science in Sports and Exercise, 15,* ix-xiii.

AMERICAN College of Sports Medicine. (1976). Position stand on weight loss in wrestlers. *Medicine and Science in Sports and Exercise, 8,* xi-xiii.

AMERICAN Dietetic Association. (1980). Nutrition and physical fitness. *Journal of the American Dietetic Association, 76,* 437-443.

AMERICAN Heart Association. (1983). Diet in the healthy child. *Circulation,* **67,** 1411A-1414A.

AMUNDSON, L. (1973). Sports medicine symposium: Weight cutting and wrestling. *South Dakota Journal of Medicine,* **26,** 31-35.

ARISTIMUNO, G., Foster, T., Voors, A., Srinivasan, S., & Berenson, G. (1984). Influence of persistent obesity in children on cardiovascular risk factors: The Bogalusa Heart Study. *Circulation,* **69,** 895-904.

ASHWELL, M. (1983). Brown adipose tissue—Relevant to obesity? *Human Nutrition: Applied Nutrition,* **37,** 232-244.

BARTA, L., Pena, M., Tichy, M., Regoly-Merei, A., Koltai, G., & Bedo, M. (1982). The effect of caffeine and physical exercise on blood lactate of obese children. *Acta Paediatrica Academiae Scientiarium Hungaricae,* **23,** 343-347.

BEUNEN, G., Malina, R., Ostyn, M., Renson, R., Simons, J., & Van Gerven, D. (1983). Fatness, growth and motor fitness of Belgian boys 12 through 20 years of age. *Human Biology,* **55,** 599-613.

BJORNTORP, P. (1983). Physiological and clinical aspects of exercise in obese persons. *Exercise and Sport Science Reviews,* **11,** 159-180.

BONNET, F. (1978). The regional growth of adipose tissue in normal and obese children. In E. Cacciari, Z. Laron, & S. Raiti (Eds.), *Obesity in childhood.* London: Academic Press.

BONNET, F., Duckerts, M., & Heuskin, A. (1976). In Z. Laron (Ed.), *The adipose child.* Basel: Karger.

BOTVIN, G., Cantlon, A., Carter, B., & Williams, C. (1979). Reducing adolescent obesity through a school health program. *Journal of Pediatrics,* **95,** 1060-1062.

BRAY, G. (1983). The energetics of obesity. *Medicine and Science in Sports and Exercise,* **15,** 32-46.

BRAY, G. (1984). Overweight is risking fate. *Western Journal of Medicine,* **140,** 779-780.

BROOK, C. (1978). The role of genetic and environmental factors in the determination of body fat in men. In E. Cacciari, Z. Laron, & S. Raiti (Eds.), *Obesity in childhood.* London: Academic Press.

BROOK C. (1983). Obesity in childhood. *Practitioner,* **227,** 213-219.

BROWN, M., Klish, W., Hollander, J., Campbell, M., & Forbes, G. (1983). A high protein, low calorie liquid diet in the treatment of very obese adolescents: Long term effect on lean body mass. *American Journal of Clinical Nutrition,* **38,** 20-31.

BROWNELL, K. (1984a). New developments in the treatment of obese children and adolescents. *Research Publications: Association for Research in Nervous and Mental Disease,* **62,** 175-183.

BROWNELL, K. (1984b). The psychology and physiology of obesity: Implications for screening and treatment. *Journal of the American Dietetic Association,* **84,** 447-450.

BROWNELL, K., & Kaye, F. (1982). A school-based behavior modification, nutrition education and physical activity program for obese children. *American Journal of Clinical Nutrition, 35*, 277-283.

BROWNELL, K., Kelman, J., & Stunkard, A. (1983). Treatment of obese children with and without their mothers: Changes in weight and blood pressure. *Pediatrics, 71*, 515-523.

BUZINA, R., Suboticanec, K., Stavljenic, A., Blagus-Pavlekovic, G., Milanovic, N., & Salzer, B. (1982). Blood pressure and blood lipids in adolescent obesity. *Human Nutrition: Clinical Nutrition, 36*, 459-467.

CANNING, H., & Mayer, J. (1968). Obesity: Analysis of attitudes and knowledge of weight control in girls. *Research Quarterly, 39*, 894-899.

CHARNEY, E., Goodman, H., & McBride, M. (1976). Childhood antecedents of adult obesity. Do chubby infants become obese adults? *New England Journal of Medicine, 295*, 6-9.

CHARZEWSKA, J., & Figurska, K. (1983). Frequency of obesity in boys aged 7-8 years in Warsaw. *Pediatria Polska, 58*, 127-131.

CHIPMAN, J., Hagan, R., & Edlin, J. (1983). Excessive weight loss in the athletic adolescent: A diagnostic dilemma. *Journal of Adolescent Health Care, 3*, 247-252.

CHRISTAKIS, G., Sajecki, S., & Hillman, R. (1966). Effect of a combined nutrition, education and physical fitness program on the weight status of obese high school boys. *Federation Proceedings, 25*, 15-19.

CIMONS, M. (1985, February 14). Obesity called "a killer" by federal panel. *The Virginian-Pilot*.

CLARKE, H. (1975). Exercise and fat reduction. *Physical Fitness Research Digest, 5*, 1-27.

COATES, T., Jeffery, R., & Slinkard, L. (1981). Heart healthy eating and exercise: Introducing and maintaining changes in health behaviors. *American Journal of Public Health, 7*, 15-23.

COLLIPP, P. (1975). Obesity programs in schools. In P. Collipp (Ed.), *Childhood obesity*. Acton, MA: Publishing Sciences Group.

COMMITTEE on Medical Aspects of Sports. American Medical Association. (1967). Wrestling and weight control. *Journal of the American Medical Association, 201*, 541-543.

COMMITTEE on Nutrition. American Academy of Pediatrics. (1983). Toward a prudent diet for children. *Pediatrics, 71*, 78-80.

COMMITTEE on Nutrition of the Mother and Preschool Child. (1978). Fetal and infant nutrition and susceptibility to obesity. *American Journal of Clinical Nutrition, 31*, 2026-2030.

COSTOM, B., & Shore, D. (1983). Effect of a comprehensive nutritional program on the growth and ponderosity of infants. *Clinical Pediatrics, 22*, 105-111.

CZINNER, A., Tichy, M., & Barta, L. (1983). Prevention of adult cardiovascular disease in obese children. *Acta Paediatrica Hungarica, 24*, 195-199.

DAHLKOETTER, J., Callahan, E., & Linton, J. (1979). Obesity and the unbalanced energy equation: Exercise versus eating habit change. *Consulting and Clinical Psychology, 47*, 898-905.

DIETZ, W. (1983). Childhood obesity: Susceptibility, cause and management. *Journal of Pediatrics, 103*, 676-686.

DIETZ, W., & Gortmaker, S. (1984). Factors within the physical environment associated with childhood obesity. *American Journal of Clinical Nutrition, 39*, 619-624.

DOTSON, C., & Ross, J. (1985). The National Children and Youth Fitness Study. Relationships between activity patterns and fitness. *Journal of Physical Education, Recreation and Dance, 56*, 86-89.

DOYARD, P., Chaussain, J., & Job, J. (1978). Adipose tissue cellularity and hormonal data in obese children. In E. Cacciari, Z. Laron, & S. Raiti (Eds.), *Obesity in childhood*. London: Academic Press.

DUSEK, D. (1982). *Thin and fit: Your personal lifestyle*. Belmont, CA: Wadsworth.

EPSTEIN, L., Koeske, R., Zidansek, J., & Wing, R. (1983). Effects of weight loss on fitness in obese children. *American Journal of Diseases of Children, 137*, 654-657.

EPSTEIN, L., & Wing, R. (1980). Aerobic exercise and weight. *Addictive Behavior, 5*, 371-388.

EPSTEIN, L., Wing, R., Kuller, L., & Becker, D. (1983). Parent-child obesity and cardiovascular risk factors. *Preventive Medicine, 12*, 437-446.

FIELDHOUSE, P. (1982). Nutrition and education of the school child. *World Review of Nutrition and Dietetics, 40*, 83-112.

FREISCHLAG, J. (1984). Weight loss, body composition, and health of high school wrestlers. *Physician and Sportsmedicine, 12*, 121-126.

FRIEDMAN, R., Kindy, P., & Reinke, J. (1982). What to tell parents about weight-loss methods. *Postgraduate Medicine, 72*, 73-75.

GARN, S., Clark, D., & Guire, K. (1975). Growth, body composition and development of obese and lean children. In M. Winick (Ed.), *Childhood obesity*, New York: John Wiley.

GILLIAM, T., Katch, V., Thorland, W., & Weltman, A. (1977). Prevalance of coronary heart disease risk factors in active children, 7 to 12 years of age. *Medicine and Science in Sports, 9*, 21-25.

GILLIAM, T.B., Thorland, W.G., & Sady, S. (1978). Blood lipids and fatness in children age 7-12. *Canadian Journal of Applied Sports Sciences, 3*, 65-69.

GREGG, W. (1970). *A boy and his physique*. Chicago: National Dairy Council.

GROLLMAN, A. (1975). Drug therapy of obesity in children. In P. Collipp (Ed.), *Childhood obesity*. Acton, MA: Publishing Sciences Group.

HAMBORG, B. (1982). Obesity and physical activity. *Scandinavian Journal of Social Medicine* (Suppl. 29), 217-220.

HAYES, A. (1984). Youth physical fitness.hearings. *Journal of Physical Education, Recreation, and Dance, 55*, 29-32, 40.

HEALD, F. (1972). Treatment of obesity in adolescence. *Postgraduate Medicine,* **51,** 109-112.

HEALD, F. (1975). Juvenile obesity. In M. Winick (Ed.), *Childhood obesity.* New York: John Wiley.

HIRSCH, J. (1972). Can we modify the number of adipose cells? *Postgraduate Medicine,* **51,** 83-86.

HIRSCH, J. (1975). Cell number and size as a determinant of subsequent obesity. In M. Winick (Ed.), *Childhood obesity.* New York: John Wiley.

HIRSCH, J., & Leibel, R. (1984). What constitutes a sufficient psychologic explanation of obesity? *Research Publications: Association for Research in Nervous and Mental Disease,* **62,** 121-130.

HO, T., Chay, S., Yie, W., Tay, J., & Wong, H. (1983). The prevalence of obesity in Singapore primary school children. *Australian Paediatric Journal,* **19,** 248-250.

HOVELS, O., Makosch, G., & Bergmann, K. (1982). Adipositas im Kindesalter. *Monatsschrift Kinderheilkunde,* **130,** 576-589.

HUBERT, H., Feinleib, M., & McNamara, P. (1983). Obesity as an independent risk factor for cardiovascular disease: A 26-year follow-up of participants in the Framingham Heart Study. *Circulation,* **67,** 968-977.

HUENEMANN, R., Hampton, M., Behnke, A., Schapiro, L., & Mitchell, B. (1974). *Teenage nutrition and physique.* Springfield, IL: C.C. Thomas.

JEQUIER, E. (1983). Does a thermogenic defect play a role in the pathogenesis of human obesity? *Clinical Physiology,* **3,** 1-7.

KELLY, P., Sullivan, D., Bartsch, M., Gracey, M., & Ridout, S. (1984). Evolution of obesity in young people of Busselton, Western Australia. *Medical Journal of Australia,* **141,** 97-99.

KNITTLE, J. (1975). Basic components in the control of childhood obesity. In M. Winick (Ed.), *Childhood obesity.* New York: John Wiley.

KNITTLE, J., & Ginsberg-Fellner, F. (1975). Can obesity be prevented? In P. Collipp (Ed.), *Childhood obesity.* Acton, MA: Publishing Sciences Group.

KNITTLE, J., Timmers, K., Ginsberg-Fellner, F., Brown, R., & Katz, D. (1979). The growth of adipose tissue in children and adolescents. *Journal of Clinical Investigation,* **63,** 239-246.

KRAWCZUK-RYBAKOWA, M., & Urban, M. (1984). Effect of low-calorie diet and exercise on certain anthropometric parameters in obese children. *Pediatria Polska,* **59,** 221-229.

LANGFORD, H. (1982). Symposium on obesity and hypertension. *Journal of Chronic Diseases,* **35,** 875-877.

LANSKY, D., & Brownell, K. (1982). Comparison of school-based treatments for adolescent obesity. *Journal of School Health,* **52,** 384-387.

LANSKY, D., & Vance, M. (1983). School-based intervention for adolescent obesity: Analysis of treatment, randomly selected control, and self-selected control subjects. *Journal of Consulting and Clinical Psychology,* **51,** 147-148.

LARON, Z., Ben-Dan, I., Shrem, M., Dickerman, Z., & Lilos, P. (1978). Puberty in simple obese boys and girls. In E. Cacciari, Z. Laron, & S. Raiti (Eds.), *Obesity in childhood*. London: Academic Press.

LAUER, R.M., Connor, W.E., & Leaverton, P.E. (1975). Coronary heart disease risk factors in school children. The Muscatine Study. *Journal of Pediatrics, 86*, 697-706.

LAVEN, G. (1982). Preventive nutrition guidelines for children. *Alabama Journal of Medical Sciences, 19*, 382-387.

LEITENBERG, H. (1976). *The handbook of behavior modification*. Englewood Cliffs, NJ: Prentice-Hall.

LITTLE, J. (1983). Management of the obese child in school. *Journal of School Health, 53*, 440-441.

LOHMAN, T. (1982). Body composition methodology in sports medicine. *Physician and Sportsmedicine, 10*, 46-58.

LOHMAN, T. (1984). Research progress in validation of laboratory methods of assessing body composition. *Medicine and Science in Sports and Exercise, 16*, 596-603.

MALLICK, M. (1983). Health hazards of obesity and weight control in children: A review of the literature. *American Journal of Public Health, 73*, 78-82.

MAHONEY, M. (1975). *Cognition and Behavior Modification*. Cambridge, MA: Ballinger.

MAHONEY, M., & Klykylo, W. (1983). An overview of anorexia nervosa, bulimia, and obesity in children and adolescents. *Journal of the American Academy of Child Psychiatry, 22*, 99-107.

MAHONEY, M., & Mahoney, K. (1970). *Permanent weight control: The total solution to the dieter's dilemma*. New York: Norton.

MANN, G. (1977). Nutrition for athletes. *Journal of the American Medical Association, 237*, 1076.

MAYER, J. (1968). *Overweight: Causes, cost and control*. Englewood Cliffs, NJ: Prentice-Hall.

MAYER, J. (1972). *Human nutrition: Its physiological, medical and social aspects*. Springfield, IL: C.C. Thomas.

MAYER, J. (1975a). Introduction. In P. Collipp (Ed.), *Childhood obesity*. Acton, MA: Publishing Sciences Group.

MAYER, J. (1975b). Obesity during childhood. In M. Winick (Ed.), *Childhood obesity*. New York: John Wiley.

MAYER, J. (Ed.). (1983). *Tufts University Diet and Nutrition Letter, 1*, 1-2.

McKENZIE, T., Buono, M., & Nelson, J. (1984). Modification of coronary heart disease (CHD) risk factors in obese boys through diet and exercise. *American Corrective Therapy Journal, 38*, 35-37.

McMINN, M. (1984). Mechanisms of energy balance and obesity. *Behavioral Neuroscience, 98*, 375-393.

MOODY, D. (1971). Fat—Fact and fancy. *DGWS research reports: Women in sports.* Washington, DC: AAHPER.

NATIONAL Dairy Council (1978). What's new in weight control? *Dairy Council Digest,* **49**, 7-12.

NUTRITION Committee, Canadian Paediatric Society. (1983). Adolescent nutrition: 3. Obesity. *Canadian Medical Association Journal,* **129**, 549-551.

OLSON, R. (Ed.). (1984). Adipocyte sizes and numbers in lean and obese subjects. *Nutrition Reviews,* **42**, 159-160.

PARIZKOVA, J. (1972). Somatic development and body composition changes in adolescent boys differing in physical activity and fitness: A longitudinal study. *Anthropologie,* **10**, 3-36.

PARIZKOVA, J. (1982). Physical training in weight reduction of obese adolescents. *Annals of Clinical Research,* **14** (Suppl. 34), 63-68.

PARIZKOVA, J., Vaneckova, M., & Vamberova, M. (1962). A study of changes in some functional indicators following reductions of excessive fat in obese children. *Physiologia Bohemoslovaca,* **11**, 351-357.

PATE, R., Ross, J., Dotson, C., & Gilbert, G. (1985). The national children and youth fitness study: The new norms. *Journal of Physical Education, Recreation and Dance,* **56**, 70-72.

PENA, M., Barta, L., Regoly-Merei, A., & Tichy, M. (1980). The influence of physical exercise upon the body composition of obese children. *Acta Paediatrica Academiae Scientiarium Hungaricae,* **21**, 9-14.

POLLOCK, M., Wilmore, J., & Fox, J. (1984). *Exercise in health and disease.* Philadelphia: W.B. Saunders.

POPA, I., Dragan, M., Georgescu, L., Deutsch, G., Otetea, G., Schmidt-Georoceanu, A., Man, I., Grigorita, M., Beligan, C., & Popa, Z. (1984). Atherogenic risk in obese and in diabetic children. *Endocrinolgie,* **22**, 61-70.

RICHMOND, D., Blyler, E., & Linscheid, T. (1983). The obese child. *American Family Physician,* **28**, 129-134.

RIENDEAU, R. (1958). Relationship of body fat to motor fitness test scores. *Research Quarterly,* **29**, 200-203.

ROCHE, A. (1984). Research progress in the field of body composition. *Medicine and Science in Sports and Exercise,* **16**, 579-583.

ROLLAND-CACHERA, M., Deheeger, M., Bellisle, F., Sempe, M., Guilloud-Bataille, M., & Patois, E. (1984). Adiposity rebound in children: A simple indicator for predicting obesity. *American Journal of Clinical Nutrition,* **39**, 129-135.

RONA, R., & Chinn, S. (1984). The national study of health and growth: Nutritional surveillance of primary school children from 1972 to 1981 with special reference to unemployment and social class. *Annals of Human Biology,* **11**, 17-28.

ROSS, J., Dotson, C., & Gilbert, G. (1985). The National Children and Youth Fitness Study: Are kids getting appropriate activity? *Journal of Physical Education, Recreation and Dance,* **56**, 82-85.

ROSS, J., Dotson, C., Gilbert, G., & Katz, S. (1985a). The national children and youth fitness study: Maturation and fitness test performance. *Journal of Physical Education, Recreation and Dance, 56*, 67-69.

ROSS, J., Dotson, C., Gilbert, G., & Katz, S. (1985b). New standards for fitness measurement. *Journal of Physical Education, Recreation and Dance, 56*, 62-66.

RUPPENTHAL, B., & Gibbs, E. (1979). Treating childhood obesity in a public school setting. *Journal of School Health, 5*, 569-571.

SADY, S., Thomson, W., Savage, M., & Petratis, M. (1982). The body composition and physical dimensions of 9 to 12-year-old experienced wrestlers. *Medicine and Science in Sports and Exercise, 14*, 244-248.

SARIS, W., Binkhorst, R., Cramwinckel, A., Van Waesberghe, F., & Van der Veen-Hezemans, A. (1980). The relationship between working performance, daily physical activity, fatness, blood lipids, and nutrition in school children. In K. Berg & B. Eriksson (Eds.), *Children and exercise IX*. Baltimore: University Park Press.

SARRIA, A. (1983). Obesidad en la adolescencia. *Anales Espandes de Pediatria, 19*, 133-144.

SARTORIUS, S., & Solberg, E. (1984). Physical management—A class to meet individual needs. *Journal of Physical Education, Recreation and Dance, 5*, 15-16.

SCAVO, D., Giovannini, C., Sellini, M., & Fierro, A. (1978). Long- and short-term results of treatment for obesity in childhood and adolescence. In E. Cacciari, Z. Laron, & S. Raiti (Eds.), *Obesity in childhood*. London: Academic Press.

SEEFELDT, V. (1984). Physical fitness in preschool and elementary school-aged children. *Journal of Physical Education, Recreation and Dance, 55*, 33-37, 40.

SHESTOWSKY, B. (1983). Ego identity development and obesity in adolescent girls. *Adolescence, 18*, 551-559.

SELTZER, C., & Mayer, J. (1970). An effective weight control program in a public school system. *American Journal of Public Health, 60*, 679-689.

SHARMAN, I. (1982). Excessive weight loss in athletes. *British Journal of Sports Medicine, 16*, 180.

SIMIC, B. (1983). Childhood obesity as a risk factor in adulthood and its prevention. *Preventive Medicine, 12*, 47-51.

SIMONSON, M. (1982). Advances in research and treatment of obesity. *Food and Nutrition News, 53*, 1-4.

SMITH, N. (1982). Nutrition and the adolescent athlete. *Current Concepts of Nutrition, 11*, 63-70.

SPAHN, U., Plenert, W., Hesse, V., Knoll, G., Petrick, E., & Kauf, E. (1982). Overnutrition and obesity in childhood as a potential risk for chronic diseases in later life. *Bibliotheca Nutritio et Dieta, 31*, 61-74.

SPRYNAROVA, J., & Parizkova, J. (1965). Changes in aerobic capacity and body composition in obese boys after reduction. *Journal of Applied Physiology, 20*, 934-937.

STALLONES, L., Mueller, W., & Christensen, B. (1982). Blood pressure, fatness, and fat patterning among USA adolescents from two ethnic groups. *Hypertension, 4*, 483-486.

STARK, O., Atkins, E., Wolff, O., & Douglas, J. (1981). Longitudinal study of obesity in the National Survey of Health and Development. *British Medical Journal*, **283**, 13-17.

STEFFER, W. (1982). The medical syndrome of obesity. *Primary Care*, **9**, 581-593.

STERN, J. (1984). Is obesity a disease of inactivity? *Research Publications: Association for Research in Nervous and Mental Disease*, **62**, 131-139.

STRAUSS, R., Lanese, R., & Malarkey, W. (1984). Decreased serum testosterone with severe weight loss among wrestlers. *Medicine and Science in Sports and Exercise*, **16**, 172.

STUNKARD, A. (1984). The current status of treatment for obesity in adults. *Research Publications: Association for Research in Nervous and Mental Diseases*, **62**, 157-173.

THOMAS, C. (Ed.) (1977). *Taber's cyclopedic medical dictionary*. Philadelphia: F.A. Davis.

THOMPSON, J., Jarvie, G., Lahey, B., & Cureton, K. (1982). Exercise and obesity: Etiology, physiology and intervention. *Psychological Bulletin*, **91**, 55-79.

TOKUNAGA, K., Ishikawa, K., Sudo, H., Matsuzawa, Y., Yamamoto, A., & Tarui, S. (1982). Serum lipoprotein profile in Japanese obese children. *International Journal of Obesity*, **6**, 399-404.

U.S. Department of Health and Human Services (1980). *Promoting health/preventing disease: Objectives for the nation*. Washington, DC: Government Printing Office.

VAN ITALLIE, T. (1984). The enduring storage capacity for fat: Implications for treatment of obesity. *Research Publications: Association for Research in Nervous and Mental Disease*, **62**, 109-119.

VAN ITALLIE, T., & Hashim, S. (1970). Obesity in an age of calorie anxiety. *Modern Medicine*, **38**, 89-96.

VASSELLI, J., Cleary, M., & Van Itallie, T. (1983). Modern concepts of obesity. *Nutrition Reviews*, **41**, 361-373.

VOBECKY, J., Vobecky, J., Shapcott, D., & Demers, P. (1983). Nutrient intake patterns and nutritional status with regard to relative weight in early infancy. *American Journal of Clinical Nutrition*, **38**, 730-738.

WARREN, M. (1984). Weight loss in athletes: Emerging health problems from medical and psychological perspectives. *Medicine and Science in Sports and Exercise*, **16**, 153.

WAXMAN, M., & Stunkard, A. (1980). Caloric intake and expenditure of obese boys. *Journal of Pediatrics*, **96**, 187-193.

WEIL, W. (1975). Infantile obesity. In M. Winick (Ed.), *Childhood obesity*. New York: John Wiley.

WEINHAUS, R. (1969). The management of obesity: Some recent concepts. *Missouri Medicine*, **66**, 719-730.

WELTMAN, A., Tran, Z., Schurrer, R., & Melcher, G. (1983). Time course of serum lipid and body composition changes seen with an intense diet, exercise and stress management program. *Medicine and Science in Sports and Exercise*, **15**, 90.

WILMORE, J. (1983). Body composition in sport and exercise: Directions for future research. *Medicine and Science in Sports and Exercise,* **15**, 21-31.

WILMORE, J.H., & McNamara, J.J. (1974). Prevalance of coronary disease risk factors in boys, 8 to 12 years of age. *Journal of Pediatrics,* **84**, 527-533.

WILSON, G. (1980). Behavior modification and the treatment of obesity. In A. Stunkard (Ed.), *Obesity.* Philadelphia: W.B. Saunders.

WINICK, M. (1974). Childhood obesity. *Nutrition Today,* **9**, 6-12.

WINICK, M. (1975). *Childhood obesity.* New York: John Wiley.

WOLMAN, P. (1984). Feeding practices in infancy and prevalence of obesity in preschool children. *Journal of the American Dietetic Association,* **84**, 436-438.

WOOLEY, S., & Wooley, O. (1984). Should obesity be treated at all? *Research Publications: Association for Research in Nervous and Mental Disease,* **62**, 185-192.

YLITALO, V. (1981). Treatment of obese school children. *Acta Paediatrica Scandinavica* (Suppl. 290), 1-108.

ZAMBRASKI, E. (1980). Weight loss for sports competition. In G. Stull (Ed.), *Encyclopedia of physical education, fitness and sports: Training, environment, nutrition and fitness.* Salt Lake City: Brighton Press.

ZIEGLER, M. (1982). Nutrition care of the pediatric athlete. *Clinics in Sports Medicine,* **1**, 371-381.

The Effects of Physical Activity
on Cardiorespiratory Fitness in Children

Christine L. Wells
Arizona State University

This paper will review research dealing with the effects of chronic exercise in children up to just beyond the age of puberty. For our purposes here, I'm going to make the arbitrary judgment that after puberty an individual is sexually mature, and consequently is no longer a child but a young adult.

There are differences in studying the effects of chronic exercise in children. In adults, we can reasonably assume that the observed physiological or performance changes that occur following chronic exercise intervention is a training response, or an adaptation to the imposed exercise program. Here, the effects of training are superimposed on a more or less stable base. In children, however, this is not the case. The physical growth and accompanying motor development and cellular maturation that naturally occur as a child grows older may be as great as or greater than the adaptations thought to result from an imposed exercise training program. Therefore, it is difficult to distinguish the effects of physical activity from the normal changes occurring with increasing age and concomitant development and maturation. While investigators often argue that control groups are not necessary in adult training studies because each subject acts as his or her own control, it is obvious that a matched control group is absolutely essential in similar studies dealing with children. Use of a matched control group is the only way to differentiate the effects of normal maturation from the effects of training in children.

The single best measure of cardiorespiratory fitness is indicated by maximal oxygen uptake, or $\dot{V}O_2$ max. $\dot{V}O_2$ max is the highest volume of oxygen that can be consumed or utilized by the body per unit time—it reflects the highest metabolic rate via oxidative or aerobic pathways that one can attain. In adults this variable is known to be highly related to endurance performance. This relationship is not nearly so strong in children, as will be discussed below, but it remains the single best measure of cardiorespiratory fitness that we have. In the following text, I will describe the variables or factors known to contribute to $\dot{V}O_2$ max, and attempt to describe the effects of growth and maturation occurring with increasing age in children as distinguished from the effects of chronic exercise.

FACTORS KNOWN TO BE RELATED TO $\dot{V}O_2$ MAX

By the Fick equation, we know that cardiac output ($\dot{Q}$) and arterial-mixed venous oxygen difference (a-$\overline{V}O_2$ diff) are factors related to $\dot{V}O_2$ max. Since the product of heart rate (HR) and stroke volume (SV) determines Q, we can assume these variables are also important to $\dot{V}O_2$ max.

It is also known that heart volume (HV) is related to SV. Respiratory ventilation volume ($\dot{V}_E$ max) is important, as are variables such as body size (height and weight), muscle mass, and amount of body fat. The quantity of red blood cells and the total body hemoglobin are important because these variables largely determine the oxygen carrying capacity of the blood. Peripheral blood flow, particularly muscle blood flow, is also important in terms of oxygen delivery to the active cells.

Basically, any factor known to influence (a) oxygen carrying capacity of the blood, (b) oxygen delivery to the metabolically active cells, and (c) cellular extraction of oxygen from the blood and oxygen utilization via an aerobic pathway—is important to cardiorespiratory fitness.

Unfortunately, there is not enough data available on all these variables in children. But, I shall briefly review what is in the literature on the above variables in regard to growth and maturation as well as training in children.

VARIABLES RELATED TO OXYGEN CARRYING CAPACITY OF THE BLOOD

Changes With Age and Growth

Blood volume (BV), hemoglobin concentration (Hb), and consequently, total hemoglobin (Hb_T) are lower in children than in adults (Åstrand, 1952; Eriksson, 1972; Bar-Or, 1983, p. 48; Shephard et al., 1969). As body size increases, however, so do these variables (see Table 1). Therefore, oxygen carrying capacity increases with age until about puberty. Testosterone is also related to the number of red blood cells and amount of hemoglobin in the blood (Mirwald & Bailey, 1981) and, in boys at least, may partially explain these changes.

Changes With Training

Total blood volume and Hb_T were higher in trained than in untrained boys (Koch & Röcker, 1977), and increased with training in 11- to 13-year-old boys (Eriksson &

Table 1

Variables Related to Oxygen Carrying Capacity

Variable	Age/Growth	Training
Blood volume	inc	inc
Hb total	inc	sl. inc
Hb conc.	inc	no change
RBCs	inc	no change

Koch, 1973). A higher blood volume enhances venous return and allows more effective heat convection from the body core to the periphery. This would indicate that training in children not only increases the total amount of oxygen carried by the blood but should also result in an improved stroke volume and improved heat tolerance as well. However, while Åstrand (1952) reported a correlation of 0.97 between $\dot{V}O_2$ max and Hb_T in children and young adults, von Döbeln and Eriksson (1972) did not.

VARIABLES RELATED TO OXYGEN DELIVERY TO METABOLICALLY ACTIVE CELLS

Changes With Age and Growth

As heart volume increases with growth, stroke volume increases and heart rate decreases at rest, submaximal exercise, and maximal exercise. Maximal cardiac output, the product of SV and HR, gradually increases with age and growth.

Lung perfusion ($\dot{Q}$) and pulmonary ventilation ($\dot{V}_E$) are directly related to oxygen delivery and so are shown in Table 2. As the thoracic cavity expands with body size, so do the respiratory muscles and, hence, respiratory capacity. Therefore, the absolute value ($1 \cdot min^{-1}$) for $\dot{V}_E$ max increases with age and body size. If maximal pulmonary ventilation is expressed relative to body weight ($1 \cdot kg^{-1} \cdot min^{-1}$), however,

Table 2

Variables Related to Oxygen Delivery to Metabolically Active Cells

Variable	Age/Growth	Training
HR	dec	submax dec max $\measuredangle$ or dec
SV	submax inc max inc	submax inc max inc
Q	submax inc max inc	submax $\measuredangle$ or dec max inc
Heart volume	inc	inc
$\dot{V}_E$ max		
$1 \cdot min^{-1}$	inc	inc
$1 \cdot kg^{-1} min^{-1}$	no change	?
Ms bl flow	dec	no change
Vent. equivalent	dec	$\measuredangle$ or dec

$\measuredangle$ = no change.

it is the same as in adults (Bar-Or, 1983, p. 30). Because of their smaller lung capacity, children have markedly higher respiratory rates than do adults performing the same task. It is interesting that pulmonary ventilation at any given oxygen uptake is higher in children, and the "ventilatory breaking point" (which signifies the onset of venous blood lactate) appears earlier than in adolescents or adults (Bar-Or, 1983, pp. 30-31). Bar-Or (1983, p. 32) reports that while some studies indicate that ventilation equivalent $\dot{V}_E/\dot{V}O_2$ decreases with age (indicating improved ventilatory efficiency), others do not. Less efficient ventilation would mean a greater oxygen cost of respiration. This may explain why children have a relatively higher metabolic cost of submaximal exercise than adults.

Muscle blood flow was found to be higher immediately after exercise in 12-year-old boys than in young adults (Koch, 1974). Subsequent studies from the same laboratory indicated that the differences diminished 1 and 4 years later (Koch, 1978, 1980). A higher muscle blood flow in children may represent a more favorable distribution of blood during exercise to compensate for a lower cardiac output (Bar-Or, 1983, p. 28). This may not be as desirable a response as it seems, however, for it may partially explain the lesser heat tolerance of children. If cutaneous blood flow is sacrificed to deliver a larger proportion of the total cardiac output to muscle, heat dissipation will be diminished.

Changes With Training

Myocardial mass (as studied by echocardiography) and heart volume (X-ray) are higher in trained than nontrained children and increase with endurance training (Allen, Goldberg, Sahn, Schy, & Wojcik, 1977; Ekblom, 1969; Eriksson & Koch, 1973; Geenen, Gilliam, Steffens, Crowley, & Rosenthal, 1981). Stroke volume at rest and at all levels of work has been shown to increase with training in pubertal children (Eriksson & Koch, 1973; Gatch & Byrd, 1979; Hamilton & Andrew, 1976), but not in prepubertal children (Hamilton & Andrew, 1976; Lind, 1970).

As is well known to occur in adults, heart rates in trained children are lower at rest and during all levels of exercise (Eriksson & Koch, 1973; Hamilton & Andrew, 1976). There is also a faster return to resting levels in the trained child. A slower heart rate reflects reduced myocardial work and oxygen uptake, leaving more reserve for muscle activity (Bar-Or, 1983, p. 49).

How does an increase in stroke volume and a decrease in heart rate affect $\dot{Q}$? At any given metabolic level, cardiac output changes very little, but maximal cardiac output increases significantly with training (Eriksson & Koch, 1973) in children as well as in adults.

Although noting that control data is notably missing in pulmonary studies in children, Bar-Or (1983, pp. 50-51) summarized training responses as a decrease in respiratory rate, an increase in tidal volume, and an increase in maximal pulmonary ventilation. Thus, with training, children become more efficient breathers. This was noted previously in a decline of ventilatory equivalent.

No change has been reported in submaximal or maximal muscle blood flow with training in 12-year-old boys (Koch, 1978). In adults, submaximal muscle blood flow decreases and maximal blood flow increases with training.

VARIABLES RELATED TO CELLULAR EXTRACTION
OF OXYGEN FROM THE BLOOD AND UTILIZATION
IN AEROBIC PATHWAYS

Changes With Age and Growth

Unfortunately, not much information is available for this group of variables in children. Arterial-venous oxygen difference (a-$\overline{V}O_2$ diff) is higher in children and therefore assumed to decrease with age. Glycogen stores provide much of the substrate for aerobic metabolism, and therefore are shown in Table 3. As muscle and liver mass increases with growth, so too does the ability to store glycogen. I have no information on age/growth changes in oxidative enzyme activity in children.

Table 3

Variables Related to Cellular Extraction of Oxygen

Variable	Age/Growth	Training
a-$\overline{V}O_2$ diff	dec	submax no change max no change
Glycogen stores	inc	inc
Oxidative enzyme activity (SDH, cytochrone oxidase, palm. CoA synthetase)	?	inc
Mitochondria	?	inc

Changes With Training

In adults, a-$\overline{V}O_2$ diff increases with training, reflecting increased peripheral oxygen extraction. In children, however, neither submaximal (Gatch & Byrd, 1979) nor maximal a-$\overline{V}O_2$ diff (Eriksson & Koch, 1973) has been reported to change with training. This discrepancy probably is due to the fact that the untrained child has a greater a-$\overline{V}O_2$ diff than the untrained adult.

Glycogen storage and oxidative enzyme activity increases following endurance conditioning in children as well as adults (Eriksson, Gollnick, & Saltin, 1974; Eriksson, Karlsson, & Saltin, 1971; Fournier et al., 1982). However, while adults show an increase in the number and volume of mitochondria with endurance training, there is no comparable information on children.

MAXIMUM AEROBIC POWER IN CHILDREN

Much of the following material comes from a review to be published soon by Krahenbuhl, Skinner, and Kohrt (1985). I am indebted to them for their willingness to share this material.

$\dot{V}O_2$ max in children has been studied extensively, and although there are many cross-sectional studies, there are also a good number of longitudinal studies (for an extensive reference list see Krahenbuhl et al., 1985). I will not differentiate between these methods of study here; basically, the longitudinal studies verify the implications of the cross-sectional studies.

Figure 1 presents $\dot{V}O_2$ max expressed in $1 \cdot min^{-1}$ in relation to chronological age in normally active children. It is readily seen that maximal oxygen uptake increases with age. The solid line presents the regression line for the boys, the dashed line is the regression line for the girls. It is obvious that these two lines are significantly different, particularly after the age of 11 or 12 years. The boys continue to increase in $\dot{V}O_2$ max with age between 6 and 16. The girls' data show slightly lower values than the boys' between ages 6 and 11, with a tendency to level off between 12 and 14, followed by a reduction after about 15 years of age. $\dot{V}O_2$ max in $1 \cdot min^{-1}$, often called absolute $\dot{V}O_2$ max, is largely a function of body mass. While girls tend to experience their adolescent growth spurt earlier than boys (around age 11 to 13 years), they stop growing in height before boys do. This means that the total growth period for boys is about 2 years longer, which accounts for their greater height. Following puberty, muscular development tends to level off for girls. Additional body mass is primarily body fat storage rather than lean body mass. During these same years, boys continue to develop their muscle and bone structure and consequently gain lean body mass. Much of the difference shown in Figure 1 reflects these sexual differences in body mass and composition.

Other functional components of the cardiorespiratory system develop somewhat differently between the sexes as well. For example, boys have a larger blood volume, a larger number of red blood cells, and more hemoglobin—due predominantly to their larger body mass. Consequently their oxygen carrying capacity is larger. Because boys have a relatively larger thorax and smaller abdominal cavity, their lung capacity and heart size differs from that of girls. This is most evident in functional differences in cardiac output, stroke volume, and heart rate. While girls most often have higher heart rates than boys, they have lower stroke volumes and thus lower cardiac output values. As boys develop greater muscle mass, it seems logical to assume that they concomitantly develop a greater capacity for glycogen storage and oxidative enzyme activity. Exactly how early in life these sexual differences become manifest, however, remains subject to debate.

Figure 2 presents the same data as Figure 1, expressed in relative terms, that is, $\dot{V}O_2$ max in ml of oxygen per kg of body weight. It is immediately evident that the relative difference between males and females increased from a negligible difference at age 6 (about 1.5%) to about a 32% difference at age 16 (Krahenbuhl et al., 1985). The most common explanation for this discrepancy is the greater accumulation of subcutaneous fat in girls, and the development of greater lean body mass in boys. While body fat contributes to body mass and must consequently be carried about, it is a less metabolically active tissue than muscle and does not contribute to oxygen uptake.

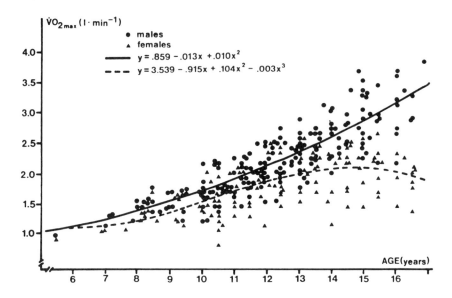

Figure 1—Relationship between $\dot{V}O_2$ max (1 · min⁻¹) and age in boys and girls 6 to 16 years of age. *Note*: From "Developmental Aspects of Maximal Aerobic Power in Children" by G.S. Krahenbuhl, J.S. Skinner, & W.M. Kohrt, 1985, *Exercise and Sport Science Reviews*.

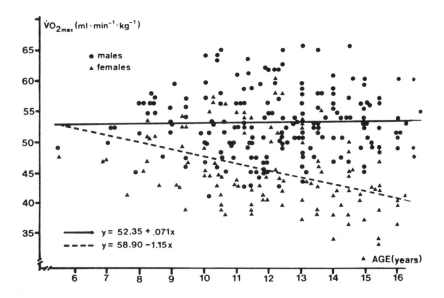

Figure 2—Relationship between $\dot{V}O_2$ max (ml · kg⁻¹ · min⁻¹) and age in boys and girls 6 to 16 years of age. *Note*: From "Developmental Aspects of Maximal Aerobic Power in Children" by G.S. Krahenbuhl, J.S. Skinner, & W.M. Kohrt, 1985, *Exercise and Sport Science Reviews*.

In addition to possible physiological differences between boys and girls that may contribute to the functional differences discussed above, a strong argument can also be made for a sociocultural basis for these differences. It can be argued that, due to different cultural expectations and the relative importance given to sport and physical activity for boys and girls, girls have not developed their potential capacity for cardiorespiratory performance to the same extent as boys have. Without elaborately exploring this topic, I believe it should be pointed out that while highly trained athletic girls far exceed the cardiorespiratory values shown in these two figures, so do highly trained athletic boys. While functional differences between highly trained boys and girls (and men and women, for that matter) are considerably reduced, they still exist.

The Effects of Training

There is an extensive literature on the training responses of children (for an extensive reference list see Krahenbuhl et al., 1985). Table 4 lists some representative studies. The majority of cross-sectional studies indicate that $\dot{V}O_2$ max values for trained groups are higher at all ages than those shown in Figures 1 and 2, with the differences being less in younger children and greater in adolescent years. A number of studies reviewed showed little or no increase in $\dot{V}O_2$ max with training before puberty, but substantial increases after puberty (Kobayashi et al., 1978; Koch, 1980; Mirwald & Bailey, 1981; Sprynarová, Párizková, & Irinová, 1978; Weber, Kartodihardjo, & Klissouras, 1976). This gives rise to the question of the relative trainability of children before and after puberty.

Some of the mixed results occurring at about the time of puberty have been explained by statements implying that younger children are less motivated to train and consequently do not give their best efforts, and that training programs for younger children are usually intermittent exercise programs that do not provide an adequate training stimulus. Mirwald and Bailey (1981) examined changes in $\dot{V}O_2$ before, during and after peak height velocity (PHV) in active and inactive boys. The most pronounced change in $\dot{V}O_2$ max occurred after mean PHV in both groups. Although this was not truly a training study, Mirwald and Bailey concluded that activity during the preadolescent period had no significant effect on $\dot{V}O_2$ max. In my opinion, a definitive study on the question of trainability before, during, and after puberty has not yet been done.

Table 4

Selected Training Studies in Children—VO₂ max

	Sex	Age	$\dot{V}O_2$ max	Mode
Brown et al., 1972	F	8-13	24-32% inc	dist. run
Lussier & Buskirk, 1977	M + F	8-13	7% inc	dist. run
Vaccaro & Clarke, 1978	M + F	9-11	17% inc	swim
Weber et al., 1976	M	10, 13, 16	10-18% inc	run, step, cycle
Eriksson & Koch, 1973	M	11-13	16% inc	dist. run
Bar-Or & Zwiren, 1973	M + F	9-10	no change	interval run
Stewart & Gutin, 1976	M	10-12	no change	interval run

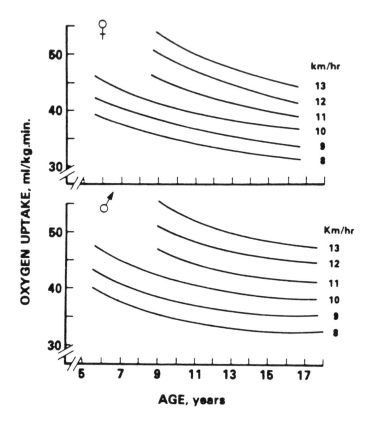

Figure 3—Relationship of submaximal oxygen uptake with age at various treadmill walking speeds. *Note*: From *Pediatric Sports Medicine for the Practitioner* (p. 8) by O. Bar-Or, 1983, New York: Springer-Verlag. Based on data from Åstrand, 1952.

Krahenbuhl et al. (1985) concluded that the maximal aerobic power of children from 8 to 14 years of age can be significantly increased following regular, intensive training. They further suggest that endurance exercise programs are more effective than intermittent exercise programs even though intermittent exercise is thought to be more characteristic of children. In the study that showed significant gains in $\dot{V}O_2$ max, there were increases of 4 to 5 ml $\cdot$ kg^{-1} $\cdot$ min^{-1}. This is an average increase of 8 to 10%, which is similar to that found in many adult training studies.

Economy of Locomotion

One of the most interesting observations about oxygen uptake in children involves what is sometimes called economy of motion or locomotion. This is best shown in Figure 3, which presents submaximal oxygen uptake of 5- to 17-year-old girls and boys walking on a treadmill at various speeds (Bar-Or, 1983, p. 8, based on Åstrand, 1952). It is seen here that the O_2 cost of walking decreases with age. At 10 km $\cdot$ hr^{-1}, for example, it costs the 5-year-old child 8 ml • kg^{-1} • min^{-1} more than the 17-year-old adolescent—a 20% difference.

Similar results were obtained for walking at different grades as shown in Figure 4 (Bar-Or, 1983, p. 9, based on Skinner et al., 1971). The higher metabolic cost in the younger child is not a result of differences in resting metabolism (which is about 1 to 2 ml • kg^{-1} • min^{-1}). It is apparently due to a wasteful, uneconomic gait (Bar-Or, 1983, p. 8). Possibly this results from the higher stride frequency required of shorter limbs (Åstrand, 1976). Several studies have shown an increase in economy of motion with training (Daniels & Oldridge, 1971; Daniels, Oldridge, Nagle, & White, 1978; Kaneko, Ito, Fuchimoto, & Toyooka, 1981). Presumably one of the performance factors changed with training is stride length. Nevertheless, the lesser economy of the younger child while walking and running largely explains why the relationship between distance-running performance and $\dot{V}O_2$ max is not as strong as in the adult (Krahenbuhl et al., 1985). Basically this means that the younger the child, the more difficult it is to predict running performance from $\dot{V}O_2$ max data.

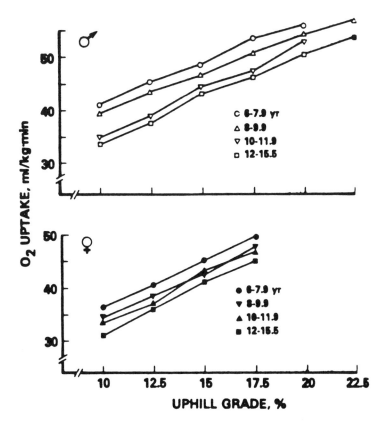

Figure 4—Oxygen cost of walking at various treadmill slopes. *Note*: From *Pediatric Sports Medicine for the Practitioner* (p. 9) by O. Bar-Or, 1983, New York: Springer-Verlag. Based on data from Skinner et al., 1971.

CONCLUSIONS

1. It is difficult to distinguish the effects of growth and maturation from the effects of training on the physiological variables related to cardiorespiratory fitness in children. An increase in general body size influences many of the functional components of cardiorespiratory fitness.

2. Although absolute values for $\dot{V}O_2$ max (l • min⁻¹) generally increase with age from 6 to 16 years, there are significant differences between boys and girls due to differences in the functional components of the cardiorespiratory system and in body composition. Relative values for $\dot{V}O_2$ max (ml • kg⁻¹ • min⁻¹) are also generally lower in girls than in boys.

3. The majority of investigations dealing with cardiorespiratory training in children report an increase in $\dot{V}O_2$ max with training. Endurance exercise appears to be more effective in increasing $\dot{V}O_2$ max than intermittent exercise. It is not yet clear whether training before puberty is as effective as training following puberty.

4. Economy of locomotion increases with age in children from 6 to 17 years of age. The corresponding decline in submaximal oxygen cost leads to more predictable distance-running performance in the older child.

REFERENCES

ALLEN, H.D., Goldberg, S.J., Sahn, D.J., Schy, N., & Wojcik, R. (1977). A quantitative echocardiographic study of champion childhood swimmers. *Circulation, 55,* 142-145.

ÅSTRAND, P.-O. (1952). *Experimental studies of physical working capacity in relation to sex and age.* Copenhagen: Ejnar Munksgaard.

ÅSTRAND, P.-O. (1976). The child in sport and physical activity: Physiology. In J.B. Albinson & G.M. Andrew (Eds.), *Child in sport and physical activity* (pp. 19-33). Baltimore: University Park Press.

BAR-OR, O. (1983). *Pediatric sports medicine for the practitioner.* New York: Springer-Verlag.

BAR-OR, O., & Zwiren, L.D. (1973). Physiological effects of increased frequency of physical education classes and of endurance conditioning on 4- to 10-year-olds girls and boys. In O. Bar-Or (Ed.), *Pediatric work physiology* (pp. 183-198). Natanya, Israel: Wingate Institute.

BROWN, C.H., Harrower, J., & Deeter, M. (1972). The effects of cross-country running on pre-adolescent girls. *Medicine and Science in Sports, 4,* 1-5.

DANIELS, J., & Oldridge, N. (1971). Changes in oxygen consumption of young boys during growth and running training. *Medicine and Science in Sports, 3,* 161-165.

DANIELS, J., Oldridge, N., Nagle, F., & White, B. (1978). Differences and changes in $\dot{V}O_2$ among young runners 10 to 18 years of age. *Medicine and Science in Sports and Exercise, 10,* 200-203.

EKBLOM, B. (1969). Effect of physical training in adolescent boys. *Journal of Applied Physiology,* **27**, 350-355.

ERIKSSON, B.O. (1972). Physical training, oxygen supply and muscle metabolism in 11-13 year old boys. *Acta Physiologica Scandinavica* (Suppl.), **384**, 1-48.

ERIKSSON, B.O., Gollnick, P.D., & Saltin, B. (1974). The effect of physical training on muscle enzyme activities and fiber composition in 11-year-old-boys. *Acta Paediatric Belgica,* **28** (Suppl.), 245-252.

ERIKSSON, B.O., Karlsson, J., & Saltin, B. (1971). Muscle metabolities during exercise in pubertal boys. *Acta Paediatrica Scandinavica,* **217** (Suppl.), 154-157.

ERIKSSON, B.O., & Koch, G. (1973). Effect of physical training on hemodynamic response during submaximal and maximal exercise in 11-13 year old boys. *Acta Physiologica Scandinavica,* **87**, 27-39.

FOURNIER, M., Ricci, J., Taylor, A.W., Ferguson, R.J., Montpetit, R.R., & Chaitman, B.R. (1982). Skeletal muscle adaptation in adolescent boys: Sprint and endurance training and detraining. *Medicine and Science in Sports and Exercise,* **14**, 453-456.

GATCH, W., & Byrd, R. (1979). Endurance training and cardiovascular function in 9- and 10-year-old-boys. *Archives of Physical Medicine and Rehabilitation,* **60**, 574-577.

GEENEN, D.L., Gilliam, T.B., Steffens, C., Crowley, D., & Rosenthal, A. (1981). The effects of exercise on cardiac structure and function in prepubescent children. *Medicine and Science in Sports and Exercise,* **13**, 93 (Abstract).

HAMILTON, P., & Andrew, G.M. (1976). Influence of growth and athletic training on heart and lung functions. *European Journal of Applied Physiology,* **36**, 27-38.

KANEKO, M., Ito, A., Fuchimoto, T., & Toyooka, J. (1981). Mechanical work and efficiency of young distance runners during level running. In A. Morecki (Ed.), *Biomechanics VII* (pp. 234-240). Baltimore: University Park Press.

KOBAYASHI, K., Kitamura, K., Miura, M., Sodeyama, H., Murase, Y., Miyashita, M., & Matsui, H. (1978). Aerobic power as related to body growth and training in Japanese boys: A longitudinal study. *Journal of Applied Physiology,* **44**, 666-672.

KOCH, G. (1974). Muscle blood flow after ischemic work and during bicycle ergometer work in boys aged 12 years. *Acta Paediatrica Belgica,* **28** (Suppl.), 29-39.

KOCH, G. (1978). Muscle blood flow in prepubertal boys. Effect of growth combined with intensive physical training. In J. Borms & M. Hebbelinck (Eds.), *Medicine and sport, vol. 11: Pediatric work physiology* (pp. 39-46). Basel: Karger.

KOCH, G. (1980). Aerobic power, lung dimensions, ventilatory capacity, and muscle blood flow in 12-16-year-old boys with high physical activity. In K. Berg & B.O. Eriksson (Eds.), *Children and exercise IX* (pp. 99-108). Baltimore: University Park Press.

KOCH, G., & Röcker, L. (1977). Plasma volume and intravascular protein masses in trained boys and fit young men. *Journal of Applied Physiology: Respiratory, Environmental and Exercise Physiology,* **43**, 1085-1088.

KRAHENBUHL, G.S., Skinner, J.S., & Kohrt, W.M. (1985). Developmental aspects of maximal aerobic power in children. In R.L. Terjung (Ed.), *Exercise and Sport Science Reviews,* **13**, 503-538.

LIND, A.R. (1970). Cardiovascular responses to static exercise. *Circulation,* **41**, 173-176.

LUSSIER, L., & Buskirk, E.R. (1977). Effects of an endurance training program on assessment of work capacity in prepubertal children. *Annals of the New York Academy of Sciences,* **301**, 734-741.

MIRWALD, R.L., & Bailey, D.A. (1981). Longitudinal comparison of aerobic power in active and inactive boys aged 7.0 to 17.0 years. *Annals of Human Biology,* **8**, 405-414.

SHEPHARD, R.J., Allen, C., Bar-Or, O., Davies, C.T.M., Degre, S., Hedman, R., Ishii, K., Kaneko, M., La Cour, J.R., di Prampero, P.E., & Seliger, V. (1969). The working capacity of Toronto schoolchildren. *Canadian Medical Association Journal,* **100**, 560-566, 705-714.

SKINNER, J.S., Bar-Or, O., Bergsteinova, V., Bell, C.W., Royer, D., & Buskirk, E.R. (1971). Comparison of continuous and intermittent tests for determining maximal oxygen intake in children. *Acta Paediatrica Scandinavica* (Suppl.), **217**, 24-28.

SPRYNAROVÁ, S., Párizková, J., & Irinová, I. (1978). Development of the functional capacity and body composition of boy and girl swimmers aged 12-15 years. In J. Borms & Hebbelinck (Eds.), *Medicine and sport; vol. 11: Pediatric work physiology* (pp. 32-38). Basel: Karger.

STEWART, K., & Gutin, B. (1976). Effects of physical training on cardiorespiratory fitness in children. *Research Quarterly,* **47**, 110-120.

VACCARO, P., & Clarke, D.H. (1978). Cardiorespiratory alterations in 9 to 11 year old children following a season of competitive swimming. *Medicine and Science in Sports and Exercise,* **10**, 204-207.

VON DÖBELN, W., & Eriksson, B.O. (1972). Physical training, maximal oxygen uptake and dimensions of the oxygen transporting and metabolizing organs in boys 11-13 years of age. *Acta Paediatrica Scandinavica,* **61**, 653-660.

WEBER, G., Kartodihardjo, W., & Klissouras, V. (1976). Growth and physical training with reference to heredity. *Journal of Applied Physiology,* **40**, 211-215.

Physical Activity, Physical Fitness, and Heart Disease Risk Factors in Children

Henry J. Montoye
University of Wisconsin–Madison

Until a few generations ago, a heart attack which might occur in middle age was considered the result of a disease that developed rapidly. With increased understanding of atherosclerosis, the disease underlying most heart attacks, it has become clear that the heart attack is the final event of a long process. Perhaps this was illustrated most forcibly by a study of 300 young men killed in the Korean War. Some 77% of these men, whose average age was 22.1 years, showed significant atherosclerosis in the coronary arteries (Enos, Beyer, & Holmes, 1953). Similar results were found in later studies of young men (Glantz & Stembridge, 1959; McNamara, Molot, Stremple, & Cutting, 1971; Rigal, Lovell, & Townsend, 1960). Fatty streaks were reported in the aortas of children many years ago (Albert, 1939; Klotz & Manning, 1911; Zeek, 1930; Zinserling, 1925) but these observations went mostly unnoticed.

Recent research has confirmed and extended these observations (Strong & McGill, 1969). Probably the most comprehensive data were those collected under the International Atherosclerosis Project in which 23,000 sets of coronary arteries and aortas from 14 countries were analyzed (McGill, 1980; McGill et al., 1968). From these data it appears that fatty streaks are present by age 3 in the aortas of almost all children, regardless of geographical area. They occur as frequently in developing nations as in the United States and other highly industrialized countries. In the coronary arteries, fatty streaks are rare before age 10 but are frequent thereafter. There is a question whether the fatty streaks in the aortas of infants are of importance, but the presence of fatty streaks in the coronary arteries in children is correlated with the incidence of raised lesions in middle age (McGill, 1980).

When it became apparent that it might be helpful to study children in order to reduce heart disease in adults, many descriptive studies of risk factors in children appeared. Space permits a review of only a few of these studies here. For example, Berenson (1980, p. 14) summarized 15 studies of serum cholesterol in pediatric populations in 9 countries in the world. The lowest concentration of cholesterol in the blood was found in the Tarahumara, a tribe of Indians who are known for their physical activity and leanness. Further description of the risk factors of this unique group may be found in Connor (1980). Similarly, Knuiman and Hautvast (1980) of the Netherlands reported the results of measuring serum total and HDL-cholesterol in 7- to 8-year-olds from 16 countries, and Saris (1982) compared data on Dutch children with those of children from other countries. Berwick, Cretin, and Keeler (1980) also summarized comparisons of many groups. Probably the largest of such studies of children in the United States have been those conducted in Bogalusa, Louisiana (Frerichs, Srinivasan, Webber, & Berenson, 1976) and in Muscatine, Iowa (Lauer, Connor, Leaverton, Reiter, & Clarke, 1975). In addition to blood lipids, most of these investigations of children also included blood pressure and body fatness.

In other studies, serum uric acid and blood glucose have been reported (Balram & Fodor, 1983), as well as smoking habits (DuRant, Linder, Harkess, & Gray, 1983; Feinleib, Kannel, Garrison, McNamara, & Castelli, 1976; Green, 1980; Hurd et al., 1980; Ibsen, Lous, & Andersen, 1982; Laakso, Rimpela, & Telama, 1979; Simons, Andersen, Simons, & Whish, 1982; Tell & Vellar, 1983; Tibblin, 1980; Williams, Carter, Arnold, & Wynder, 1979). Children's attitudes and knowledge of smoking as it relates to health have been reported (Green, 1980; Simons et al., 1982). Attempts have even been made to study type A behavior in children (Gerace et al., 1983; Hunter, Parker, Williamson, Webber, & Berenson, 1983; Nora, 1980).

Habitual physical activity is also now being studied in children (Andersen, Masironi, Rutenfranz, & Seliger, 1978; Durnin, 1971; Engstrom, 1980; Gilliam, Freedson, Geenan, & Shahraray, 1981; LaPorte et al., 1982; MacConnie, Gilliam, Geenen, & Pels, 1982; Rutenfranz, Berndt, & Knauth, 1972; Saris, 1982; Seliger, Trefny, Bartunkova, & Pauer, 1974; Verschuur, Kemper, & Besseling, 1984) but methods still leave much to be desired.

In recent years, "tracking"in children of the most common coronary heart disease (CHD) risk factors has been reported (Berenson, 1980, pp. 394-395; Berenson, Srinivasan, & Webber, 1980; Boulton, 1981, pp. 56-67; Cresanta, Webber, Srinivasan, & Berenson, 1983b; Costello, Disney, Dodson, & Bush, 1983; Feinleib, Garrison, & Havlik, 1980; Fixler, Fayers, Laird, & deSwiet, 1983; Lauer & Clarke, 1980; Linder & DuRant, 1982; Primary Prevention of Essential Hypertension, 1983; Webber, Baugh, Cresanta, & Berenson, 1983). Tracking looks for consistency of the risk factor over time. In general, children who are at the high end of a distribution continue to retain their relative position as they grow older. To my knowledge, consistency has not been studied insofar as physical activity is concerned. Studies are now beginning to appear that attempt to modify the risk factors in children (Gorman, 1977; Jaycox, Baranowski, Nader, Dworkin, & Vanderpool, 1983; McKenzie, Buono, & Nelson, 1984; Williams, Arnold, & Wynder, 1977).

Risk factors in children are more prevalent in countries where the incidence of coronary heart disease in adults is high (Connor, 1980; Kannel, 1976). Even within a single country, the presence of risk factors was correlated with the CHD mortality rate of different regions (Balram & Fodor, 1983). In general, risk factors in children are high if their parents' risk factors are also high or if a parent died from CHD at a young age (Feinleib et al., 1976; Glueck, Fallat, Tsang, & Buncher, 1974; Ibsen et al., 1982; Linder & DuRant, 1982). I'm aware of only one study in which physical activity of children of fathers who died at a young age from CHD was compared with the activity of other children. In this case the activity of both groups of children was not significantly different (Ibsen et al., 1982).

In general, CHD risk factors (other than physical activity) are only moderately correlated in families (Berenson, 1980; pp. 325-326; Cresanta, Baugh, Voors, Webber, & Berenson, 1983a; Deutscher, Epstein, & Kjelsberg, 1966; Feinleib et al., 1980; French, Dodge, & Kjelsberg, 1967; Glueck, 1982; Hardell, 1981; Higgins, Kjelsberg, & Metzner, 1967; Johnson, Epstein, & Kjelsberg, 1965; Linder & DuRant, 1982; Montoye, Metzner, & Keller, 1975; Namboordiri et al., 1983). This list of references is not exhaustive, but the studies listed illustrate the point. It is interesting that there is no correlation in blood pressure between adopted children living together or between parents and adopted children (Primary Prevention of Essential Hypertension, 1983). Only a brief report has appeared to date in which physical activity has been studied in families (Cook, Adams, LaPorte, Spina, & Metz, 1984).

RISK FACTORS, HABITUAL PHYSICAL ACTIVITY, AND PHYSICAL FITNESS

Body Fatness

Many studies have compared risk factors for coronary heart disease in groups of *adults* who vary in their habitual physical activity. With the exception of one risk factor, body fatness, there have been relatively few investigations of this kind in *children*. With regard to obesity or body fatness, it has been generally demonstrated that fat children are less active than lean children. A few examples of such studies are Ishiko, Ikeda, and Enomoto (1968); Johnson, Burke, and Mayer (1956); Parizkova (1974); Saris, Binkhorst, Cramwinckel, Van Der Veen-Hezemans, and van Waesberghe (1979); and Stefanki, Heald, and Mayer (1959). However, there have been a few reports in which leaner children were not found to be more active, as pointed out in the review by Thompson, Jarvie, Lahey, and Cureton (1982).

Another approach in studying the relationship of coronary risk factors is an experimental one, namely, increasing the amount of exercise in children and measuring change, if any, in risk factors. That an increase in physical activity in children, particularly in obese children, can cause a reduction in fatness is well known (Brownell & Kaye, 1982; Bryant, Garett, & Dean, 1984; Dwyer, Coonan, Leitch, Hetzel, & Baghurst, 1983; Fisher & Brown, 1982; Parizkova, 1963, 1982; Parizkova, Vaneckova, Sprynarova, & Vamberova, 1971; Thompson et al., 1982; Vlasek, Hart, & Seitz, 1983).

Some investigators have studied the relationship of physical fitness to risk factors for CHD. However, a low score on a fitness test does not necessarily mean inactivity. If the studies by Klissouras (1971, 1972, 1973) and Klissouras, Pirnay, and Petit (1973) are to be accepted, physical fitness is mainly inherited. Nevertheless, one's fitness can be improved with an increase in exercise training, and children who are more active tend to be capable of a greater work capacity. Even though there are problems in measuring fitness in children, the difficulties are not as great as those encountered in trying to assess physical activity. Most investigators would expect risk factors to be more closely related to an estimate of the circulatory-respiratory capacity, namely $\dot{V}O_2$ max, than to other aspects of fitness such as strength and balance. However, in some instances it is not possible to measure $\dot{V}O_2$ max, and another measurement is used, for example work capacity, heart rate response to a standard exercise, or PWC_{170}.

Body fatness has long been known to be inversely related to $\dot{V}O_2$ max or work capacity in children. A few typical investigations are the following: Fraser, Phillips, and Harris (1983); Gilliam, Katch, Thorland, and Weltman (1977); Mocellin and Rutenfranz (1971); Montoye, (1975, p. 98); Parizkova et al. (1971); Saris (1982); Williams et al. (1979); and Wilmore and McNamara (1974).

Blood Pressure

Only a few investigations of the relationship of blood pressure to habitual physical activity in children have been reported. Fixler (1978) found no significant relationship between the two in 8th-grade children (about 13 years of age). Similarly, Kemper (1980) reported that the blood pressure of active 13- and 14-year-old boys was not significantly different from that of less active boys of the same age. He used a questionnaire and pedometers to measure physical activity. Aerobic power was significantly higher in the active boys.

Exercise training programs generally have been found to produce little change in blood pressure in children. Pate and Blair (1978) concluded in their review of studies on this subject that significant changes in blood pressure following an exercise program have not been demonstrated in children. Linder, DuRant, and Mahoney (1983) exercised 25 white males, ages 11 to 17, 30 minutes per day, 4 days per week for 8 weeks. Although their physical working capacity increased, their blood pressures did not change significantly when compared to 25 control subjects. Similarly, 4 months of training of 9 children, ages 11 to 13, did not result in significant changes in resting or exercise blood pressures (Eriksson & Koch, 1973). In the investigation by Bryant et al. (1984), although the mean resting blood pressures of 16 children decreased after 12 weeks of exercise, the change was not statistically significant (no control group was used in the study). In another investigation, despite a significant increase in work capacity following 14 weeks of increased physical activity in 166 10-year-old boys and girls, their resting blood pressures did not change significantly compared to 162 controls (Dwyer et al., 1983).

The one exception to these investigations was the study of Fisher and Brown (1982), who reported a significant decrease in diastolic blood pressure in 7th-graders (about age 12 to 13) who exercised 30 minutes per day, 5 days per week for 12 weeks. These subjects also increased their endurance on a treadmill test. The control group did not change in either blood pressure or work capacity. Reductions in blood pressure occurred in obese children (McKenzie et al., 1984) and in children with relatively high blood pressure (Frank, Farris, Ditmarsen, Voors, & Berenson, 1982). But these were multi-intervention studies involving not only an exercise program but dietary changes and medications, and thus it is not possible to determine the effects of exercise.

In studying the relationship of blood pressure to physical fitness it must be remembered that, as in adults, body fatness in children may be related to blood pressure (Berchtold, Sims, Horton, & Berger, 1983; Boulton, 1981; Fraser et al., 1983; Montoye, 1975, p. 102; Williams et al., 1979). Therefore, it is important to try to eliminate the influence of body fatness on the relationship of blood pressure to physical fitness. Table 1 contains a summary of studies of the relationship of resting blood pressure and physical fitness measurements. If the effects of body fatness are removed in some way, there appears to be only a suggestion of a relationship (negative) between physical fitness and blood pressure. Of course, it is possible that one's physical fitness as a child could be related to one's blood pressure later in life, but this has apparently not been studied. In the Tecumseh, Michigan, high school, students were allowed to select physical education, band, art, or music as one of their courses. Those who were more physically fit and leaner tended to select physical education, but the systolic and diastolic blood pressures of this group were not statistically different from the group that elected one of the other courses (Montoye, 1975, p. 108).

Table 1

Physical Fitness Versus Blood Pressure in Children: Literature Review

Subjects and age (yrs)	Phys. fit. measure	Blood pressure	Correlation coefficient	Reference
95 boys, 8-12	$\dot{V}O_2$ max	systolic	$-.21\ p < .05$	Wilmore &
95 boys, 8-12	$\dot{V}O_2$ max	diastolic	$-.16$	McNamara (1974)
755 boys 9-18	Speed in	systolic	$-.35$ to $+.37$[a]	Montoye, p. 107
749 boys, 9-18	600-yd	diastolic	$-.20$ to $+.10$[a]	(1975)
629 girls, 9-18	run	systolic	$-.16$ to $+.20$[a]	
626 girls, 9-18		diastolic	$-.24$ to $+.27$[a]	
101 boys, 8-18	PWC$_{150}$	systolic	$.13$[b]	Boulton (1981)
96 girls, 8-18	PWC$_{150}$	systolic	$-.15$[b]	
127 preadolescents				Fraser, Phillips, &
boys	PWC$_{170}$	systolic	sig. neg.[c]	Harris (1983)
		diastolic	NS[c]	
girls	PWC$_{170}$	systolic	NS[c]	
		diastolic	NS[c]	
93 adolescents				
boys	PWC$_{170}$	systolic	sig. neg.[c]	
		diastolic	NS[c]	
girls	PWC$_{170}$	systolic	sig. neg.[c]	
		diastolic	NS[c]	

[a]Effect of age, height and weight removed.
[b]Effect of height, weight, fatness, and pubertal stage removed.
[c]Effect of age, skinfold, height and arm lean mass removed.

Smoking

Smoking in children as related to habitual physical activity has also received only limited attention. In a survey of 2,831 Finnish children, Laakso et al. (1979) found that a significantly higher percentage of inactive boys and girls smoked daily than did more active children. The data were collected by questionnaire. One must wonder if all children who smoke admit this fact; perhaps smoking practices in children should be assessed by biochemical methods.

Blood Lipids

Blood lipids in children have been studied more extensively than blood pressure and smoking, but the numbers of subjects are still usually small. Figure 1 shows a comparison of active and inactive children in serum total cholesterol and triglycerides. There was no significant difference in serum total cholesterol (TC) in any of these studies nor in an investigation by Kemper (1980) when active and inactive 13- and 14-year-olds were compared. The only exception was a report by Pucsok and Martos (1984),

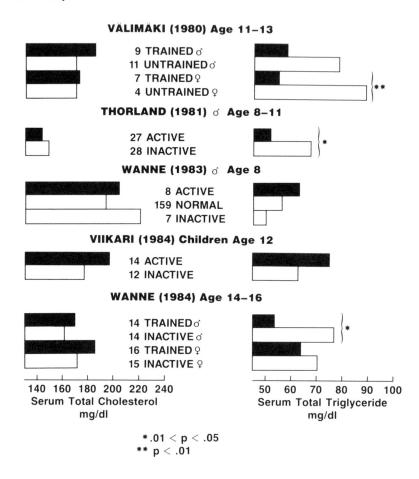

Figure 1 — Summary of studies comparing serum total cholesterol and triglyceride in active (trained) with inactive (untrained) children. In the investigation by Thorland and Gilliam (1981), the influence of body fatness in the comparison was eliminated. Unless indicated with an asterisk, the differences were statistically insignificant.

who found significantly lower TC in 16 trained compared to 20 untrained adolescent boys. The TC of 24 trained adolescent girls was not significantly different from that of untrained girls. The fact that in most of these studies the comparisons were not corrected for body fatness probably is unimportant because there appears to be little or no correlation between body fatness and TC in children (Berenson et al., 1980; DuRant, Linder, & Mahoney, 1983; Gilliam et al., 1977; Gilliam, Thorland, Sady, & Weltman, 1978; Välimäki, Hursti, Pihlaskoski, & Viikari, 1980; Wanne et al., 1983; Wilmore & McNamara, 1974; Ylitalo, 1981).

Resting serum total triglycerides seem to be lower in active compared to inactive or untrained children, but this was not a uniform finding (Figure 1). As with serum TC, there is little or no relationship between body fatness and serum triglycerides (DuRant, Linder, & Mahoney, 1983; Gilliam et al., 1977; Välimäki et al., 1980; Wilmore & McNamara, 1974; Ylitalo, 1981).

The study of serum high-density cholesterol (HDL-C) and the ratio of HDL-C or TC appears more promising. A summary of studies comparing active with less active children in shown in Figure 2. Although Wanne et al. (1983) found no significant difference in HDL-C or in the ratio HDL-C/TC among activity groups, he reported that children who received higher grades in physical education had significantly higher values in these measurements. Pucsok and Martos (1984) also report higher HDL-C and HDL-C/TC in 41 trained compared to 44 untrained children.

Birk, Quan, Dillingham, Schroeder, and Fahey (1981), Välimäki et al. (1980), and Wanne, Viikari, and Välimäki (1984) reported that fatter children had significantly lower HDL-C than leaner ones. The correlation coefficients ranged from − .20 to − .49. Others, however, have reported no significant relationship between the two measurements in children (DuRant, Linder, & Mahoney, 1983; DuRant, Linder, Harkess, &

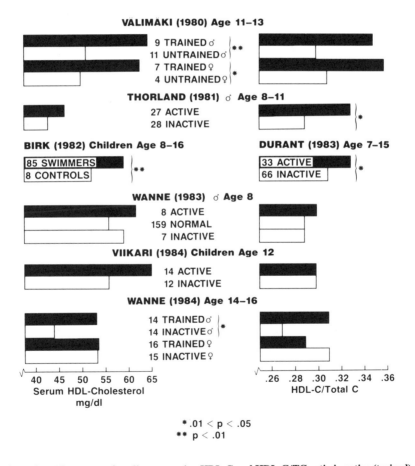

Figure 2 — Summary of studies comparing HDL-C and HDL-C/TC ratio in active (trained) with inactive (untrained) children. In the investigation by Thorland and Gilliam (1981) the influence of body fatness was eliminated. In the study by DuRant et al. (1983, p. 58) the influences of sex and age were removed. Unless indicated with an asterisk, the differences were statistically insignificant.

Gray, 1983; Sady, Berg, Beal, & Smith, 1981; Ylitalo, 1981). There is even less evidence of a relationship between fatness and the ratio HDL-C/TC (DuRant, Linder, & Mahoney, 1983; DuRant, Linder, Harkess, & Gray, 1983; Välimäki et al., 1980; Ylitalo, 1981).

The effects of an exercise program on blood lipids have also received some attention. Unfortunately, only a few studies have employed adequate controls. Hunt and White (1980) reported that a 10-week exercise program for teenage males (mean age 18.1) had no effect on serum TC or triglycerides or on HDL-C or low-density cholesterol (LDL-C) in a study involving 15 boys each in moderate and heavy exercise groups and 10 in the control group. However, this study also showed no improvement in $\dot{V}O_2$ max in any group, so there is no evidence of a training effect. In the study of Linder, DuRant, Gray, and Harkess (1979) 103 black children, ages 7 to 15, were assigned at random to either an exercise or control group. The exercise program lasted 4 weeks, but no other details are given. No significant changes in any blood lipids were observed. In a later study, Linder et al. (1983) compared 25 boys, ages 11 to 17, who exercised aerobically 4 days per week for 8 weeks, with a control group of 25 boys of the same age. The exercise group improved in work capacity whereas the control group did not. There was no evidence that body fatness changed in either group, nor was there a significant change in any of the blood lipids.

Nizankowska-Blaz and Abramowicz (1983) compared TC and triglyceride and HDL-C and LDL-C in 38 children, mean age 14.4 years, who had been training in a sport school for 3 years, with 35 children of the same mean age in a standard school. The sport school children received 10 periods of exercise per week, compared to 2 periods in the standard school. There are no pretraining values and the sport school children had about the same TC and LDL-C as the standard school children, but the former had higher HDL-C (52 vs. 45 mg/dl) and lower serum total triglycerides (69 vs. 80 mg/dl). No data are given on work capacity or body fatness. Dwyer et al. (1983) reported no effect on blood lipids in 10-year-old children when the amount of physical education was increased for 14 weeks from 1 hour and 15 minutes per week to 6 hours and 15 minutes per week. However, details are lacking for a complete evaluation. In the study by Fisher and Brown (1982), 38 7th-graders (ages 12 and 13) were randomly assigned to an exercise, exercise and diet, diet only, or control group. The first two groups participated in 30 minutes per day, 5 days per week of vigorous physical activity. After 12 weeks, TC and body fatness decreased and work capacity increased in the first two groups. The "exercise only" group also increased in HDL-C and HDL-C/TC ratio. The only change in the diet group was a significant decrease in TC. The control group didn't change in any of the measurements.

There have been other experimental studies in which no controls were used for comparison. Widhalm, Maxa, and Zyman (1978) reported a decrease in TC and no change in HDL-C in obese children but, besides the lack of controls, the children were placed on 1,000 kcal/day diets and the experiment lasted only 3 weeks. The training program in the study by Gilliam and Burke (1978) lasted twice as long but also lacked controls. The subjects were 14 girls, 8 to 10 years of age, who exercised for 40 minutes per day, 6 days per week. There was no change after 6 weeks in TC, but HDL-C and the ratio HDL-C/TC increased significantly, which is a frequent finding in studies of adults. Bryant et al. (1984) exercised 16 children ages 6 to 16 three times per week for 12 weeks. Each child had at least one coronary risk factor. There was a significant improvement in work capacity and a significant decrease in body fatness. Although TC decreased on the average by about 11 mg/dl, the change was not statistically significant. There was no control group. In an investigation of obese children without a control group, Ylitalo (1981, 1984) reported that an exercise program together with dietary changes, including a reduction in calories, resulted in a decrease in fatness and an improvement in work capacity in one group of the children. TC or triglyceride did not change significantly but the HDL-C and HDL-C/TC increased in this group. However, since there were dietary changes, it is difficult to determine if exercise had any effect.

Tables 2a and 2b contain a summary of studies in children in which physical fitness was compared to TC. In the modified Harvard Step Test, a high score (i.e., high heart rate) indicates poor fitness. Clearly, regardless of how the work or cardiovascular-respiratory capacity is estimated, it is not correlated with TC, particularly when the effect of body fatness is removed. As with blood pressure, children in Techumseh High School who selected physical education did not have different concentrations of TC in their blood than those who selected another subject (Montoye, 1975, p. 163). Table 3 indicates there also is little or no relationship between physical fitness and serum total triglycerides in children.

Whereas HDL-C has generally been reported to be higher in more fit adults (Howley et al., 1982), there is not strong evidence that this holds true for children (see Table 4). There is a suggestion that fitness and HDL-C is related, but the relationship is not impressive. Since LDL-C tends to be lower and HDL-C to be higher in more fit children, the ratio HDL-C/TC appears to differentiate a little better between fit and unfit children than either measurement alone (Table 5), but again the differences are not impressive.

Blood Glucose and Uric Acid

Glucose tolerance and serum uric acid are sometimes also considered risk factors for CHD. We found glucose tolerance to be unrelated to physical fitness in normal children (Table 6). Glucose tolerance was no different in children who elected physical education in high school from those who elected other courses (Montoye, 1975, p. 167). Ylitalo (1981, 1984) did report that in obese children serum insulin was significantly higher 2 hours after a glucose challenge than in more fit children, confirming earlier studies (Björntorp, 1977). This observation has also been reported recently in obese children (Dover et al., 1984). High insulin levels have been reported to be an independent risk factor for coronary heart disease (Ylitalo, 1984).

The effects of exercise training on blood glucose and glucose tolerance in normal *adults* have been studied a number of times with inconclusive results. These investigations have been reviewed elsewhere (Montoye, Block, Metzner, & Keller, 1977). To my knowledge, similar studies have not been done in normal children. For many years exercise has been one of the treatment modalities in diabetes (Montoye, Block, Metzner, & Keller, 1977), and it is known that the insulin requirement is reduced if a program of regular exercise is followed. Diabetic control appears to improve with exercise (Ludvigsson, 1980). However, there is little data in the literature on the long-range effects of training with adequate controls, even among diabetic children (Koivisto &

Table 2a

Physical Fitness Versus Serum Total Cholesterol in Children: Literature Review

Subject and age (yrs)	Physical fitness measure	Correlation coefficient	Reference
95 boys, 8-12	$\dot{V}O_2$ max	-.18	Wilmore & McNamara (1974)
699 boys, 9-18	Speed on	-.36 to +.25[a,b]	Montoye, p. 165 (1975)
564 girls, 9-18	600-yd run	-.37 to +.14[a]	
869 boys, 10-19	Modified Harvard	-.08 to +.18[c]	Montoye et al. (1976)
791 girls, 10-19	Step Test	-.02 to -.11	
47 children, 7-12	$\dot{V}O_2$ max	-.04	Gilliam et al. (1977)
285 boys, 10-19	$\dot{V}O_2$ max	.08[d]	Montoye, Block, & Gayle
44 girls, 10-19	$\dot{V}O_2$ max	-.06[d]	(1978)
20 boys, 11-13	Bicycle erg. perf.	.35	Välimäki et al. (1980)
11 girls, 11-13		.19	
93 children, 14-16	Bicycle erg. perf.	-.09	Wanne et al. (1984)

[a]Age-specific partial rs, effect of weight and height removed.
[b]Two partial rs of 10 were statistically significant, $p < .05$.
[c]Partial rs in 2 year-age groups, effect of skinfolds removed.
[d]Partial rs, effect of age, weight, and skinfolds removed.

Table 2b

Physical Fitness Versus Serum Total Cholesterol in Children: Literature Review

Subjects and age (yrs)	Physical fitness measure	Mean cholesterol mg/dl		Sig. of diff.	Reference
		Fit 75th percentile	Unfit 25th percentile		
171 children, 4-6	PWC$_{170}$	183	187	NS	Saris et al. (1979)
54 children, 8-12					
2,658 children, 10-15	Modified Harvard Step Test	156	161[a]	$p < .05$	Williams et al. (1979)
372 boys, 6	$\dot{V}O_2$ max	155	166	$p < .01$	Saris (1982)
359 girls, 6		170	159	$p < .05$	
427 boys, 8		166	166	NS	
447 girls, 8		166	178	$p < .05$	
368 boys, 10		170	174	NS	
426 girls, 10		182	182	NS	

[a]Below 17th percentile rather than below 25th percentile.

Table 3

Physical Fitness Versus Serum Triglycerides in Children: Literature Review

Subjects and age (yrs)	Physical fitness measure	Mean triglycerides (mg/dl) Fit 75th percentile	Unfit 25th percentile	Sig. of diff.	Correlation coefficient	Reference
95 boys, 8-12	$\dot{V}O_2$ max				-.23*	Wilmore & McNamara (1974)
47 children, 7-12	$\dot{V}O_2$ max				-.30	Gilliam et al. (1977)
285 boys, 10-19	$\dot{V}O_2$ max				.05[a]	Montoye, Block, & Gayle (1978)
44 girls, 10-19	$\dot{V}O_2$ max				-.05[a]	
20 boys, 11-13	Bicycle erg. perf.				-.13	Välimäki et al. (1980)
11 girls, 11-13					-.83**	
93 children, 14-16	Bicycle erg. perf.				-.08	Wanne et al. (1984)
171 children, 4-6	PWC170	69	66	NS		Saris et al. (1979)
54 children, 8-12	PWC170	86	68	NS		

[a]Partial r, effect of age, weight, and skinfolds removed.
* p < .05.
** p < .01.

Table 4

Physical Fitness Versus HDL-Cholesterol in Children: Literature Review

Subjects and age (yrs)	Physical fitness measure	Correlation coefficient	Reference
20 boys, 11-13	Bicycle erg. perf.	.53*	Välimäki et al. (1980)
11 girls, 11-13		.51	
53 obese children, 7-14	Bicycle erg. perf.	.30*	Ylitalo (1981, 1984)
51 children, 6-12	V̇O₂ max.	Not related[a]	Sady et al. (1981)
50 boys, 11-17	Bicycle erg. perf.	−.09	DuRant, Linder, & Mahoney (1983, p. 238)
93 children, 11-16	Bicycle erg. perf.	.00	Wanne et al. (1984)

		Mean HDL-C (mg/dl)			
		Fit 75th percentile	Unfit 25th percentile	Sig. of diff.	
171 children, 4-6	PWC₁₇₀	52	51	NS	Saris et al. (1979)
54 children, 8-12		53	52	NS	
372 boys, 6	V̇O₂ max	54	54	NS	
339 girls, 6		58	50	p < .01	
427 boys, 8	V̇O₂ max	54	54	NS	Saris (1982)
447 girls, 8		54	54	NS	
368 boys, 10	V̇O₂ max	58	54	NS	
426 girls, 10		58	50	p < .01	

[a]Partial r, effect of fatness removed, not statistically significant.
*p < .05.

Table 5

Physical Fitness Versus HDL-Cholesterol/Total Cholesterol Ratio in Children: Literature Review

Subjects and age (yrs)	Physical fitness measure	Correlation coefficient	Mean HDL-C/TC Fit 75th percentile	Unfit 25th percentile	Sig. of diff.	Reference
20 boys, 11-13	Bicycle erg. perf. Work/body wt.	.20				Välimäki et al. (1980)
11 girls, 11-13	Bicycle erg. perf. Work/body wt.	.37				
53 obese children, 7-14	Bicycle erg. perf.	.39**				Ylitalo (1981, 1984)
50 boys, 11-17	Bicycle erg. perf.	.01				DuRant, Linder, & Mahoney (1983, p. 238)
93 children, 14-16	Bicycle erg. perf.	.04				Wanne et al. (1984)
342 boys, 6	$\dot{V}O_2$ max		0.36	0.35	$p < .05$	Saris (1982)
339 girls, 6			0.34	0.32	$p < .01$	
427 boys, 8			0.34	0.32	$p < .05$	
447 girls, 8			0.33	0.30	$p < .01$	
368 boys, 10			0.34	0.31	$p < .01$	
426 girls, 10			0.32	0.28	$p < .001$	

**$p < .01$.

Table 6

Physical Fitness Versus Glucose Tolerances in Children: Literature Review

Subjects and age (yrs)	Physical Fitness measure	Correlation coefficient	Reference
725 boys, 9-18 583 girls, 9-18	Speed in 600-yd run	− .20 to + .18[a] − .39 to + .12[ab]	Montoye, p. 166 (1975)
848 boys, 10-19 759 girls, 10-19	Modified Harvard Step Test	+ .06 to + .15[bc] + .08 to + .23[cd]	Montoye, Block, Keller, & Willis (1977)
274 boys, 10-19 41 girls, 10-19	$\dot{V}O_2$ max $\dot{V}O_2$ max	− .02[e] − .35[e]	Montoye, Mikkelsen, Block, & Gayle (1978)

[a]Age specific partial *rs*, effect of weight and height removed.
[b]One partial *r* of 10 statistically significant, $p < .05$.
[c]Partial *rs* in 2 year-age groups, effect of skinfolds removed.
[d]Two partial *rs* of 10 statistically significant, $p < .05$.
[e]Partial *r*, effect of age, weight, and skinfolds removed.

Table 7

Physical Fitness Versus Serum Uric Acid in Children: Literature Review

Subject and age (yrs)	Physical fitness measure	Correlation coefficient	Reference
536 boys, 9-18	Speed in	$-.26$ to $+.21$[a]	Montoye, p. 147 (1975)
454 girls, 9-18	600-yd run	$-.38$ to $+.15$[a]	
789 boys, 10-19	Modified Harvard	.01 to .17[bc]	Montoye, Mikkelsen, Willis,
710 girls, 10-19	Step Test	.00 to .11[b]	& Keller (1975)
274 boys, 10-19	$\dot{V}O_2$ max	.02[d]	Montoye, Mikkelsen, Block,
41 girls, 10-19	$\dot{V}O_2$ max	.40[d**]	& Gayle (1978)

[a]Age specific partial rs, effects of weight and height removed, one statistically significant, $p < .05$.
[b]Partial rs in 2-year age groups, effect of skinfolds removed.
[c]Two partial rs of five, statistically significant, $p < .05$.
[d]Partial r, effects of age, weight, and skinfolds removed.
**$p < .01$.

Groop, 1982). Concerning diabetic boys, LaPorte, Dorman, and Drash (1984) made the interesting observation that participation in team sports in high school was associated with lower mortality in early adult life. It is possible, of course, that fewer of the severe cases (and hence those more likely to die early) participated in athletics.

High concentration of serum uric acid is associated with gout, a disease of protein, particularly purine, metabolism. People affected with gout have a higher than normal incidence of coronary heart disease. Hence, elevated concentrations of serum uric acid had been suggested as a risk factor in coronary heart disease. However, as Table 7 indicates, physical fitness does not appear to be associated with serum uric acid in children. Also, serum uric acid concentration was not significantly different in children who elected physical education in high school compared to those who did not (Montoye, 1975, p. 146).

CONCLUSIONS

The results presented in this review are disappointing. However, one should keep in mind that in adults also, the results of research relating habitual physical activity or physical fitness to most CHD risk factors is equivocal. It is true, of course, that active adults are generally leaner, and increasing one's exercise usually results in some loss in body fat. On the other hand, differences between active and inactive people are not so apparent with regard to other risk factors such as blood pressure, serum total cholesterol or triglycerides, glucose tolerance, serum uric acid, or blood clotting or lysis time. The one exception appears to be serum HDL-C and its percentage of TC, both of which seem to be higher in active adults. Physical fitness for muscular work in adults has not been shown to be an important correlate of CHD risk factors, again with the exceptions of body fatness and possibly HDL-C and HDL-C/TC. Therefore, it should not be surprising that the relationship of physical activity or physical fitness to CHD risk factors in children appears to be unimpressive.

It might be that CHD risk factors simply are not closely related to exercise habits or work capacity. It is possible, for example, that exercise does not have a profound effect on the development of atherosclerosis in human beings, but that a program of vigorous activity may permit some people to live longer in spite of atherosclerosis.

Before we settle on this conclusion, however, we should examine the state of the art in research with children more closely. There are many difficulties in assessing habitual physical activity in adults, but these difficulties are even greater with children. Among adults, one's occupation frequently accounts for much of the variation in habitual physical activity among men and women. However, in children it is the use of their leisure time that determines how active they are, and this activity is more difficult to assess than is occupational activity. Also, during much of the year when a child's life is more regimented in school, there may be less opportunity for variation in physical activity. In addition, as we grow older the environment has more time to exert its influence on the CHD risk factors, resulting in a greater variance in these measures among adults. Thus, the smaller variance in physical activity and risk factors in children make it more difficult to show correlation between the two.

The measurement of work capacity or $\dot{V}O_2$ max generally requires an all-out effort, and hence motivation and cooperation. Many young children don't understand "maximal effort," probably because they have not experienced it. Therefore, an investigator is often not sure when maximum work capacity has been measured in children. Inaccuracies in this regard vitiate the correlation with CHD risk factors.

Exercise may require a long period of time to produce an effect on risk factors. A 10- or 12-year-old boy or girl has not lived long enough to have exercised regularly and strenuously for very long. Some adults, on the other hand, have exercised for many years. For example, adult tennis players in our study (Howley et al., 1982) had been playing regularly for an average of 40 years.

Time also works in another way. Perhaps risk factors and physical fitness in children are determined primarily by inheritance and family environment. As the children grow older and leave home, the environment outside the home is able to exert greater influence. This is related to the smaller variance in children discussed above. The result is greater difficulty of demonstrating an effect of exercise in children.

What can be suggested for future research? Certainly we should continue to study the effects of exercise on risk factors in children, for several reasons. In the first place, with regard to some risk factors, there is a paucity of data on children in the literature. Second, the numbers are still small in some analyses. Third, the statistical analyses in many instances are not as complete in children, for example, removing the influence of body fatness or other confounding variables. Fourth, our methods of measuring habitual physical activity and physical fitness in children must be improved.

Our understanding of serum lipids is increasing. It now appears important to study lipoproteins of different densities—even separating HDL-C into its subfractions. Relationships of exercise and fitness to these lipid subclassifications should be studied. Perhaps we should not expect much effect of physical activity if the risk factor (blood pressure, cholesterol, etc.) is normal. It might be better to single out those children with high values and study the effects of exercise on this population.

Finally, I would like to suggest what is, in my opinion, a more fundamental question than any of the others: Can physical educators influence children to remain active in later life, and if so, how? As far as I know, this question has not been studied with an appropriate research design.

REFERENCES

ALBERT, Z. (1939). Die Veränderungen der Aorta bei Kindern und ihr Verhaltnis zur Atherosklerose. *Virchow's Archiv fur Pathologische Anatomie und Physiologie, 303*, 265-279.

BALRAM, B.C., & Fodor, J.G (1983). Coronary heart disease risk factors in Newfoundland children. *CVD Epidemiology Newsletter, 33*, 53.

BERCHTOLD, P., Sims, E.A., Horton, E.S., & Berger, M. (1983). Obesity and hypertension: Epidemiology, mechanisms, treatment. *Biomedicine and Pharmacotherapy, 37*, 251-258.

BERENSON, G.S. (1980). *Cardiovascular risk factors in children.* Oxford: Oxford University Press.

BERENSON, G.S., Srinivasan, S.R., & Webber, L.S. (1980). Prognostic significance of lipid profiles in children. In R.M. Lauer & R.B. Shekella (Eds.), *Childhood prevention of atherosclerosis and hypertension.* (pp. 75-86). New York: Raven Press.

BERWICK, D.M., Cretin, S., & Keeler, E.B. (1980). *Cholesterol, children, and heart disease.* New York/Oxford: Oxford University Press.

BIRK, T., Quan, A., Dillingham, C., Schroeder, R., & Fahey, T. (1981). *Plasma HDL-cholesterol and body composition of swimmers aged 8-16 years.* Presented at annual meeting of AAHPERD.

BJÖRNTORP, P. (1977). Exercise in the treatment of obesity. *Clinical Endocrinology,* **5**, 431-453.

BOULTON, J. (1981). Nutrition in childhood and its relationships to early somatic growth, body fat, blood pressure, and physical fitness. *Acta Pediatrica Scandinavica* (Suppl. 284), 1-85.

BROWNELL, K.D., & Kaye, F.S. (1982). A school-based behavior modification, nutrition education, and physical activity program for obese children. *American Journal of Clinical Nutrition,* **35**, 277-283.

BRYANT, J.G., Garett, H.L., & Dean, M.S. (1984). Coronary heart disease. The beneficial effects of exercise to children. *Journal of the Louisiana State Medical Society,* **136**, 15-17.

CONNOR, W.E. (1980). Cross-cultural studies of diet and plasma lipids and lipoproteins. In R.M. Lauer & R.B. Shekella (Eds.), *Childhood prevention of atherosclerosis and hypertension.* (pp. 99-111). New York: Raven Press.

COOK, T., Adams, L., LaPorte, R., Spina, R., & Metz, K. (1984). Familial aggregation of cardiovascular risk factors and physical activity. *Medicine and Science in Sports and Exercise,* **16**, 169. (Abstract)

COSTELLO, C., Disney, G., Dodson, W., & Bush, M. (1983). Longitudinal study of the incidence and persistence of obesity in girls from ages 9 to 16 years. *Federation Proceedings,* **42**, 535. (Abstract)

CRESANTA, J.L., Baugh, J.G., Voors, A.W., Webber, L.S., & Berenson, G.S. (1983a). Parent-child interactions of cardiovascular disease risk factors in a biracial community—the Bogalusa heart study. *CVD Epidemiology Newsletter,* **33**, 41.

CRESANTA, J.L., Webber, L.S., Srinivasan, S.R., & Berenson, G.S. (1983b). Tracking of lipoprotein cholesterol in children over a six year period. *CVD Epidemiology Newsletter,* **33**, 41.

DEUTSCHER, S., Epstein, F.H., & Kjelsberg, M.O. (1966). Familial aggregation of factors associated with coronary heart disease. *Circulation,* **33**, 911-924.

DOVER, E.V., Davis, J.M., Lampert, R., Lampert, M., Caldwell, C., Rocchio, L., & Goodyear, L. (1984). The effect of a seven-week program of physical training on glucose hemostasis in obese children. *Medicine and Science in Sports and Exercise,* **16**, 173. (Abstract)

DURANT, R.H., Linder, C.W., Harkess, J.W., & Gray, R.G. (1983). The relationship between physical activity and serum lipids and lipoproteins in black children and adolescents. *Journal of Adolescent Health Care,* **4**, 55-60.

DURANT, R.H., Linder, C.W., & Mahoney, O.M. (1983). Relationship between habitual physical activity and serum lipoprotein levels in white male adolescents. *Journal of Adolescent Health Care,* **4**, 235-240.

DURNIN, J.V.G.A. (1971). Physical activity of adolescents. *Acta Paediatrica Scandinavica* (Suppl. 217), 133-135.

DWYER, T., Coonan, W.E., Leitch, D.R., Hetzel, B.S., & Baghurst, R.A. (1983). An investigation of the effects of daily physical activity on the health of primary school students in South Australia. *International Journal of Epidemiology, 12*, 308-313.

ENGSTROM, L.M. (1980). Physical activity of children and youth. *Acta Paediatrica Scandinavica* (Suppl. No. 283), 101-105.

ENOS, W.F. Jr., Beyer, J.C., & Holmes, R.H. (1953). Pathogenesis of coronary disease in American soldiers killed in Korea. *Journal of the American Medical Association, 152*, 1090-1093.

ERIKSSON, B.O., & Koch, G. (1973). Effect of physical training on hemodynamic response during submaximal and maximal exercise. *Acta Physiologica Scandinavica, 87*, 27-39.

FEINLEIB, M., Garrison, R.J., & Havlik, R.J. (1980). Environmental and genetic factors affecting the distribution of blood pressure in children. In R.M. Lauer & R.B. Shekella (Eds.), *Childhood Prevention of Atherosclerosis and Hypertension.* (pp. 271-279). New York: Raven Press.

FEINLEIB, M., Kannel, W.B., Garrison, R.J., McNamara, P., & Castelli, W.P. (1976). Relation of parental history of coronary heart disease to risk factors in young adults. *Circulation, 54*, Part II, 52. (Abstract)

FISHER, H.G., & Brown, M. (1982). The effects of diet and exercise on selected coronary risk factors in children. *Medicine and Science in Sports and Exercise, 14*, 171. (Abstract)

FIXLER, D.E. (1978). Epidemiology of childhood hypertension. In W.B. Strong (Ed.), *Atherosclerosis: Its pediatric aspects* (chap. 9). New York: Grune and Stratton.

FIXLER, D.E., Fayers, P., Laird, W.P., & deSwiet, M. (1983). Trends in systolic blood pressure during childhood and adolescence. *CVD Epidemiology Newsletter, 33*, p. 46.

FRANK, G.C., Farris, R.P., Ditmarsen, P., Voors, A.W., & Berenson, G.S. (1982). An approach to primary prevention treatment for children with high blood pressure in a total community. *Journal of the American College of Nutrition, 1*, 357-374.

FRASER, G.E., Phillips, R.L., & Harris, L.R. (1983). Physical fitness and blood pressure in school children. *Circulation, 67*, 405-412.

FRENCH, J.G., Dodge, H.J., & Kjelsberg, M.O. (1967). A study of familial aggregation of serum uric acid levels in the population of Techumseh, Michigan, 1959-60. *American Journal of Epidemiology, 86*, 214-224.

FRERICHS, R.R., Srinivasan, S.R., Webber, L.S., & Berenson, G.S. (1976). Serum cholesterol and triglyceride levels in 3,446 children from a biracial community: The Bogalusa heart study. *Circulation, 54*, 302-309.

GERACE, T., Smith, J.C., Christakis, G., Kafatos, A., Trakas, D., & Stangos, L. (1983). Prevalence of type A in young males in rural and urban mainland Greece and Crete. *CVD Epidemiology Newsletter, 33*, 16.

GILLIAM, T.B., & Burke, M.B. (1978). Effects of exercise on serum lipids and lipoproteins in girls, ages 8 to 10 years. *Artery, 4*, 203-213.

GILLIAM, T.B., Freedson, P.S., Geenan, D.L., & Shahraray, B. (1981). Physical activity patterns determined by heart rate monitoring in 6-7-year-old children. *Medicine and Science in Sports and Exercise*, **13**, 65-67.

GILLIAM, T.B., Katch, V.L., Thorland, W., & Weltman, A. (1977). Prevalence of coronary heart disease risk factors in active children, 7 to 12 years of age. *Medicine and Science in Sports*, **9**, 21-25.

GILLIAM, T.B., Thorland, W.G., Sady, S., & Weltman, A.L. (1978). Blood lipids and fatness in children, ages 7-13. *Canadian Journal of Applied Sports Sciences*, **3**, 65-69.

GLANTZ, W.M., & Stembridge, V.A. (1959). Coronary artery atherosclerosis as a factor in aircraft accident fatalities. *Journal of Aviation Medicine*, **30**, 75-89.

GLUECK, C.J. (1982). Cradle-to-grave atherosclerosis: High density lipoprotein cholesterol. *Journal of the American College of Nutrition*, **1**, 41-48.

GLUECK, C.J., Fallat, R.W., Tsang, R., & Buncher, C.R. (1974). Hyperlipemia in progeny of parents with myocardial infarction before age 50. *American Journal of Diseases of Children*, **127**, 70-75.

GORMAN, W.F. (1977). Childhood sloth and gluttony causing heart attacks. *Arizona Medicine*, **34**, 467-468.

GREEN, D.E. (1980). Beliefs of teenagers about smoking and health. In R.M. Lauer & R.B. Shekalla (Eds.), *Childhood prevention of atherosclerosis and hypertension*. (pp. 223-228). New York: Raven Press.

HARDELL, L.I. (1981). Serum lipids and lipoproteins at birth and in early childhood. *Acta Paediatrica Scandinavica* (Suppl. 285), 1-29.

HIGGINS, M.W., Kjelsberg, M., & Metzner, H. (1967). Characteristics of smokers and nonsmokers in Tecumseh, Michigan. I. The distribution of smoking habits in persons and families and their relationship to social characteristics. *American Journal of Epidemiology*, **86**, 45-59.

HOWLEY, E.T., Gayle, R.C., Montoye, H.J., Painter, P., Fleshood, L., Endres, J., & Sundahl, L. (1982). HDL-cholesterol in senior tennis players. *Scandinavian Journal of Sports Sciences*, **4**, 44-48.

HUNT, H.F., & White, J.R. (1980). Effects of ten weeks of vigorous daily exercise on serum lipids and lipoproteins in teenage males. *Medicine and Science in Sports and Exercise*, **12**, 93. (Abstract)

HUNTER, S.M., Parker, P., Williamson, D., Webber, L.S., & Berenson, G.S. (1983). Type A behavior pattern and observed hyperactivity in children—Bogalusa heart study. *CVD Epidemiology Newsletter*, **33**, 42.

HURD, P.D., Johnson, C.A., Pechacek, T., Bast, L.P., Jacobs, D.R., & Luepker, R. (1980). Prevention of cigarette smoking in seventh grade students. *Journal of Behavioral Medicine*, **3**, 15-28.

IBSEN, K.K., Lous, P., & Andersen, G.E. (1982). Coronary heart risk factors in 177 children and young adults whose fathers died from ischemic heart disease before age 45. *Acta Paediatrica Scandinavica*, **71**, 609-613.

ISHIKO, T., Ikeda, N., & Enomoto, Y. (1968). Obese children in Japan. *Research Journal of Physical Education*, **12**, 168-174.

JAYCOX, S., Baranowski, T., Nader, P.R., Dworkin, R., & Vanderpool, N.A. (1983). Theory-based health education activities for third to sixth grade children. *Journal of School Health*, **53**, 584-585.

JOHNSON, B.C., Epstein, F.H., & Kjelsberg, M.O. (1965). Distributions and family studies of blood pressure and serum cholesterol levels in a total community—Tecumseh, Michigan. *Journal of Chronic Diseases*, **18**, 147-160.

JOHNSON, M.L., Burke, B.S., & Mayer, J. (1956). Relative importance of inactivity and overeating in the energy balance of obese high school girls. *American Journal of Clinical Nutrition*, **4**, 37-44.

KANNEL, W.B. (1976). Prospects for prevention of atherosclerosis in the young. *Australian and New Zealand Journal of Medicine*, **6**, 410-419.

KEMPER, H.C.G. (1980). Growth and health of adolescents. *Geneeskunde en Sport*, **13**, 18. Quoted by W.H.M. Saris (1982), *Aerobic power and daily physical activity in children* (p. 10). Nijmegen, The Netherlands: Krips.

KLISSOURAS, V. (1971). Heritability of adaptive variation. *Journal of Applied Physiology*, **31**, 338-344.

KLISSOURAS, V. (1972). Genetic limit of functional adaptability. *International Zeitschrift fur angewante Physiologie*, **30**, 85-94.

KLISSOURAS, V. (1973). Prediction of potential performance with reference to heredity. *Journal of Sports Medicine and Physical Fitness*, **13**, 100-107.

KLISSOURAS, V., Pirnay, F., & Petit, M. (1973). Adaptations to maximal effort: Genetics and age. *Journal of Applied Physiology*, **35**, 288-293.

KLOTZ, O., & Manning, M.F. (1911). Fatty streaks in the intima of arteries. *Journal of Pathology and Bacteriology*, **16**, 211-220.

KNUIMAN, J.T., & Hautvast, J.G.A.J. (1980). Serum total and HDL cholesterol in schoolboys from 16 countries. *CVD Epidemiology Newsletter*, **29**, 86.

KOIVISTO, V.A., & Groop, L. (1982). Physical training in juvenile diabetes. *Annuals of Clinical Research* (Suppl. 34), **14**, 74-79.

LAAKSO, L., Rimpela, M., & Telama, R. (1979). Relationship between physical activity and some other health habits among Finnish youth. *Schriftenreihe des Bundesintitutus fur Sportwissenschaft*, **36**, 76-81.

LaPORTE, R.E., Cauley, J.A., Kinsey, C.M., Corbett, W., Robertson, R., Black-Sandler, R., Kuller, L.H., & Falkel, J. (1982). The epidemiology of physical activity in children, college students, middle-aged men, menopausal females and monkeys. *Journal of Chronic Diseases*, **35**, 787-795.

LaPORTE, R.E., Dorman, J.S., & Drash, A. (1984). Physical activity and diabetic complications: A follow-up study of 735 patients with insulin-dependent diabetes. *Medicine and Science in Sports and Exercise*, **16**, 732. (Abstract)

LAUER, R.M., & Clarke, W.R. (1980). Immediate and long-term prognostic significance of childhood blood pressure levels. In R.M. Lauer & R.B. Shekella (Eds.), *Childhood prevention of atherosclerosis and hypertension.* New York: Raven Press.

LAUER, R.M., Connor, W.E., Leaverton, P.E., Reiter, M.A., & Clarke, W.R. (1975). Coronary heart disease risk factors in school children: The Muscatine study. *Journal of Pediatrics,* **86**, 697-700.

LINDER, C.W., & DuRant, R.H. (1982). Exercise, serum lipids, and cardiovascular disease-risk factors in children. *Pediatric Clinics of North America,* **29**, 1341-1354.

LINDER, C.W., DuRant, R.H., Gray, R.G., & Harkess, J.W. (1979). The effect of exercise in serum lipid levels in children. *Clinical Research,* **27**, 797. (Abstract)

LINDER, C.W., DuRant, R.H., & Mahoney, O.M. (1983). The effect of physical conditioning on serum lipids and lipoproteins in white male adolescents. *Medicine and Science in Sports and Exercise,* **15**, 232-236.

LUDVIGSSON, J. (Ed.) (1980). Physical exercise in the treatment of juvenile diabetes mellitus. *Acta Paediatrica Scandinavica* (Suppl. 283), 1-122.

MacCONNIE, S.E., Gilliam, T.B., Geenen, D.L., & Pels, A.E., III. (1982). Daily physical activity patterns of prepubertal children involved in a vigorous exercise program. *International Journal of Sports Medicine,* **3**, 202-207.

McGILL, H.C., Jr. (1980). Morphologic development of the atherosclerotic plaque. In R.M. Lauer & R.R. Shekelle (Eds.), *Childhood prevention of atherosclerosis and hypertension* (p. 44). New York: Raven Press.

McGILL, H.C., Jr., Arias-Stellen, J., Carbonnell, L.M., Correa, P., deVeyra, E.A., Donoso, S., Eggen, D.A., Galindo, L., Guzman, M.A., Lichtenberger, E., Loken, A.C., McGarry, P.A., McMahan, C.A., Montenegro, M.R., Mossy, J., Perez-Iamayo, R., Restrepo, C., Robertson, W.B., Salas, J., Solberg, L.A., Strong, J.P., Tejada, C., & Wainwright, J. (1968). General findings of the international atherosclerosis project. *Laboratory Investigation,* **18**, 466-502.

McKENZIE, T.L., Buono, M., & Nelson, J. (1984). Modification of coronary heart disease (CHD) risk factors in obese boys through diet and exercise. *American Corrective Therapy Journal,* **38**, 35-37.

McNAMARA, J.J., Molot, M.A., Stremple, J.F., & Cutting, R.T. (1971). Coronary artery disease in combat casualties in Vietman. *Journal of the American Medical Association,* **216**, 1185-1187.

MOCELLIN, R., & Rutenfranz, J. (1971). Investigations of the physical working capacity of obese children. *Acta Paediatrica Scandinavica* (Suppl. 217), 77-79.

MONTOYE, H.J. (1975). *Physical activity and health: An epidemiologic study of an entire community.* Englewood Cliffs, NJ: Prentice-Hall.

MONTOYE, H.J., Block, W., & Gayle, R. (1978a). Maximal oxygen uptake and blood lipids. *Journal of Chronic Diseases,* **31**, 111-118.

MONTOYE, H.J., Block, W., Keller, J.B., & Willis, P.W., III. (1976). Fitness, fatness, and serum cholesterol: An epidemiologic study in an entire community. *Research Quarterly,* **47**, 400-408.

MONTOYE, H.J., Block, W., Keller, J.B., & Willis, P.W., III. (1977). Glucose tolerance and physical fitness: An epidemiologic study in an entire community. *European Journal of Applied Physiology, 37*, 237-242.

MONTOYE, H.J., Block, W.D., Metzner, H., & Keller, J.B. (1977). Habitual physical activity and glucose tolerance: Males age 16-64 in a total community. *Diabetes, 26*, 172-176.

MONTOYE, H.J., Metzner, H.L., & Keller, M.O. (1975). Familial aggregation of strength and heart rate response to exercise. *Human Biology, 47*, 17-36.

MONTOYE, H.J., Mikkelsen, W.M., Block, W.D., & Gayle, R. (1978). Relationship of oxygen uptake capacity, serum uric acid and glucose tolerance in males and females, age 10-69. *American Journal of Epidemiology, 108*, 274-282.

MONTOYE, H.J., Mikkelsen, W.H., Willis, P.W., III, & Keller, J.B. (1975). Serum uric acid, body fatness, and heart rate response to exercise. *Medicine and Science in Sports, 7*, 233-236.

NAMBOODIRI, K., Morrison, J., Green, P., Kaplan, E., Glueck, C.J., & Rifkind, B. (1983). Familial association of high density lipoprotein cholesterol (HDL-C): The collaborative lipid research clinics (LRC) family study. *CVD Epidemiology Newsletter, 33*, 29.

NIZANKOWSKA-BLAZ, T., & Abramowicz, T. (1983). Effects of intensive physical training on serum lipids and lipoproteins. *Acta Paediatrica Scandinavica, 72*, 357-359.

NORA, J.J. (1980). Identifying the child at risk for coronary heart disease as an adult: A strategy for prevention. *Journal of Pediatrics, 97*, 706–711.

PARIZKOVA, J. (1963). Impact of age, diet, and exercise on man's body composition. *Annals of the New York Academy of Science, 110*, 661-674.

PARIZKOVA, J. (1974). Particularities of lean body mass and fat development in growing boys as related to their motor activity. *Acta Paediatric Belgique* (Suppl. 28), 233-243.

PARIZKOVA, J. (1982). Physical training in weight reduction of obese adolescents. *Annals of Clinical Research, 34*, 63-68.

PARIZKOVA, J., Vaneckova, M., Sprynarova, S., & Vamberova, M. (1971). Body composition and fitness in obese children before and after special treatment. *Acta Paediatrica Scandinavica* (Suppl. 217), 80-85.

PATE, R.R., & Blair, S.N. (1978). Exercise and the prevention of atherosclerosis: Pediatric implications. In W.B. Strong (Ed.), *Atherosclerosis: Its pediatric aspects* (pp. 251-286). New York: Grune & Stratton.

PRIMARY prevention of essential hypertension. (1983). Geneva, Switzerland: World Health Organization Technical Report Series 686.

PUCSOK, J., & Martos, E. (1984). Physical performance and plasma lipids in trained and untrained adolescents. 1984 Olympic Congress, Eugene, Oregon, *Biomechanics-Kinanthropometry and Sports Medicine, Exercise Science Section* (pp. 98-99). (Abstract)

RIGAL, R.D., Lovell, F.W., & Townsend, F.M. (1960). Pathologic findings in the cardiovascular systems of military flying personnel. *American Journal of Cardiology,* **6**, 19-25.

RUTENFRANZ, J., Berndt, I., & Knauth, P. (1974). Daily physical activity investigated by time budget studies and physical performance capacity of schoolboys. *Acta Paediatrica Belgica,* **28** (Suppl.), 79-86.

SADY, S.P., Berg, K., Beal, D., & Smith, J.L. (1981). Relation between high density lipoprotein cholesterol and body fatness or aerobic power in 6-12 year old boys and girls. *Medicine and Science in Sports and Exercise,* **13**, 106. (Abstract)

SARIS, W.H.M. (1982). *Aerobic power and daily physical activity in children.* Nijmegen, The Netherlands: Krips.

SARIS, W.H.M., Binkhorst, R.A., Cramwinckel, A.B., Van Der Veen-Hezemans, A.M., & van Waesberghe, F. (1979). Evaluation of somatic effects of health education program for schoolchildren. *Bibliotheca Nutrito et Dieta (Basel),* **27**, 77-84.

SELIGER, V., Trefny, Z., Bartunkova, S., & Pauer, M. (1974). The habitual activity and physical fitness of 12 year old boys. *Acta Paediatrica Belgica,* **25** (Suppl.), 54-59.

SIMONS, L.A., Andersen, N., Simons, J., & Whish, P. (1982). Health attitudes and knowledge, and coronary risk factors in high-school children. Sidney and Inverell. *Medical Journal of Australia,* **21**, 178-183.

STEFANKI, P.A., Heald, F.P., & Mayer, J. (1959). Caloric intake in relation to energy output in obese and non-obese adolescent boys. *American Journal of Clinical Nutrition,* **7**, 55-62.

STRONG, P., & McGill, H.C., Jr. (1969). The pediatric aspects of atherosclerosis. *Journal of Atherosclerosis Research,* **9**, 251-265.

TELL, G.S., & Vellar, O.D. (1983). CVD risk factors related to pubertal development: The Oslo youth study. *CVD Epidemiology Newsletter,* **33**, 21.

THOMPSON, J.K., Jarvie, G.J., Lahey, B.B., & Cureton, K.J. (1982). Exercise and obesity: Etiology, physiology, and intervention. *Psychological Bulletin,* **91**, 55-79.

THORLAND, W.G., & Gilliam, T.B. (1981). Comparison of serum lipids between habitually high and low active pre-adolescent males. *Medicine and Science in Sports and Exercise,* **13**, 316-321.

TIBBLIN, G. (1980). Raising a smoke-free generation in Sweden. In R.M. Lauer & R.B. Shekella (Eds.), *Childhood prevention of atherosclerosis and hypertension* (pp. 454-458). New York: Raven Press.

VÄLIMÄKI, I., Hursti, M.L., Pihlaskoski, L., & Viikari, J. (1980). Exercise performance and serum lipids in relation to physical activity in schoolchildren. *International Journal of Sports Medicine,* **1**, 132-136.

VERSCHUUR, R., Kemper, H.C.G., & Besseling, C.W.M. (1984). Habitual physical activity and health in 13 and 14 year old teenagers. In J. Ilmarinen & I. Valimaki (Eds.), *Children and sport.* Berlin: Springer-Verlag.

VIIKARI, J., Välimäki, I., Telama, R., Siren-Tiusanen, H., Anderblom, H.K., Dahl, M., Lahde, P.L., Personsen, M., Pietikainen, M., Sudninen, P., & Uhari, M. (1984). Atherosclerosis precursors in Finnish children. In J. Ilmarinen & I. Välimäki (Eds.), *Children and sport*, Berlin: Springer-Verlag.

VLASEK, I.W., Hart, S.S., & Seitz, G. (1983). Fatness changes in adolescent summer campers. *Medicine and Science in Sports and Exercise*, **15**, 180. (Abstract)

WANNE, O., Viikari, J., Telama, R., Åkerblom, H.K., Pesonen, E., Uhari, M., Dahl, M., Suoninen, P., & Välimäki, I. (1983). Physical activity and serum lipids in 8 year old Finnish school boys. *Scandinavian Journal of Sports Science*, **5**, 10-14.

WANNE, O., Viikari, J., & Välimäki, I. (1984). Physical performance and serum lipids in 14-16 year old trained, normally active, and inactive children. In J. Ilmarinen & I. Välimäki (Eds.), *Children and sport*. Berlin: Springer-Verlag.

WEBBER, L.S., Baugh, J.G., Cresanta, J.L., & Berenson, G.S. (1983). Transition of cardiovascular risk factors from adolescence to young adulthood: The Bogalusa post high school study. *Circulation* (Suppl. II), pp. 111-160.

WIDHALM, K., Maza, E., & Zyman, H. (1978). Effect of diet and exercise upon cholesterol and triglyceride content of plasma lipoproteins in overweight children. *European Journal of Pediatrics*, **127**, 121-126.

WILLIAMS, C.L., Arnold, C.B., & Wynder, E.L. (1977). Primary prevention of chronic disease beginning in childhood. *Preventive Medicine*, **6**, 344-357.

WILLIAMS, C.L., Carter, B.J., Arnold, C.B., & Wynder, E.L. (1979). Chronic disease risk factors among children. The "know your body" study. *Journal of Chronic Diseases*, **32**, 505-513.

WILMORE, J.H., & McNamara, J.J. (1974). Prevalence of coronary heart disease risk factors in boys, 8 to 12 years of age. *Journal of Pediatrics*, **84**, 527-533.

YLITALO, V. (1981). Treatment of obese schoolchildren. *Acta Paediatrica Scandinavica* (Suppl. 290), 1-108.

YLITALO, V.M. (1984). Exercise performance and serum lipids in obese schoolchildren before and after a reconditioning program. In J. Ilmarinen & I. Välimäki (Eds.), *Children and sport* (pp. 247-254). Berlin: Springer-Verlag.

ZEEK, P. (1930). Juvenile arteriosclerosis. *Archives of Pathology*, **10**, 417–446.

ZINSERLING, W.D. (1925). Untersuchungen über Atherosklerose. 2. Uber die Aortaverfettung bei Kindern. *Vierchow's Archiv fur Pathologische Anatomie und Physiologie*, **255**, 677-705.

Health-Related Fitness Levels of American Youth

Margaret J. Safrit
University of Wisconsin–Madison

Evidence of the widespread interest in physical fitness in this country cannot be disputed, even though many Americans continue to be inactive. The general public has become better informed about the benefits of exercise, and many lay persons are aware of the currently recommended exercise prescriptions for the frequency, duration, and intensity of exercise. It might seem logical to assume that this awareness is also reflected in physical education classes in the public schools and that American youth are therefore becoming fitter. The purpose of this paper is to examine the status of youth fitness in this country and to discuss perceptions of physical education teachers about health-related physical fitness.

Although physical fitness has been defined in many ways, the primary focus of this paper will be *health-related* physical fitness—aspects of fitness that are related to and predictive of health. This type of fitness can be contrasted with motor fitness or athletic ability, which reflect fitness necessary to participate in athletic events. In developing the Health-Related Physical Fitness Test (AAHPERD, 1980, 1984), three components of health-related physical fitness were identified: cardiorespiratory endurance, body composition, and musculoskeletal function of the low back/abdominal area. These components were scientifically documented as affecting one's health state, able to be changed through physical activity, and measurable in a psychometrically defensible way. This was accepted as an operational definition of health-related physical fitness. The underlying theme of this conceptual approach was that physical fitness should have a definition that is meaningful across the life span. In other words, health-related fitness should have the same meaning for a 7-year-old girl as it does for an 80-year-old man.

HEALTH-RELATED BENEFITS OF PHYSICAL ACTIVITY

Why is health-related physical fitness important for the young child? The risk factors associated with coronary disease have been well documented in adult populations. However, this paper is a review of the fitness status of children and youth. How reasonable is it to assume that these risk factors are also present in young children? There have been a number of studies in this area using children as subjects. Several risk factors such as hypertension, elevated blood lipids, obesity, and physical inactivity have been identified in children (Gilliam, Katch, Thorland, & Weltman, 1977; Gilliam, Thorland, & Sady, 1978; Gilliam, Freedson, MacConnie, Geenen, & Pels, 1981; Wilmore & McNamara, 1974). This topic is covered more thoroughly in other papers published in this volume. Certainly there is sufficient evidence to suggest that proper monitoring of diet and physical activity ought to be stressed in the young child.

LARGE-SCALE STUDIES OF YOUTH FITNESS

What evidence is there of the level of health-related physical fitness in our schoolchildren? Although much has been written about fitness, only four large-scale studies have been undertaken in the past 10 years. Three of these studies were conducted to provide normative data on a battery of tests. These were the Youth Fitness Test study in 1976, the Nabisco/Amateur Athletic Union (AAU) study,[1] and the Health-Related Physical Fitness Test (HRPFT) study in 1980. Since the Youth Fitness Test and the test used in the Nabisco/AAU study are primarily tests of both athletic performance-related fitness and health-related fitness, they will not be reviewed here. The fourth study, the National Children and Youth Fitness Study (NCYFS), was published in 1985 by the U.S. Department of Health and Human Services. One of the primary purposes of this study was to assess the fitness levels of American youth.

Both the HRPFT and NCYF studies used a measure of fitness that has been validated on the basis of empirical research and/or clinical evidence. This was the Health-Related Physical Fitness Test, consisting of four subtests: (a) distance run test, a measure of cardiorespiratory function, (b & c) bent-knee timed sit-ups and sit-and-reach test, both measures of abdominal/low back musculoskeletal function, and (d) sum of skinfolds, a measure of body composition. The NCYF study added one item to this battery—a chin-ups test, a measure of arm and shoulder girdle strength.

There were four major differences in the design of these two studies. First, the HRPFT used a convenience sample of physical education students whose teachers volunteered to collect normative data. The NCYFS, on the other hand, used a national probability sample which included students who may or may not have been in physical education classes (Errecart, Ross, Gilbert, & Ghosh, 1985). Second, in the HRPFT study, skinfold data were not collected. Rather, data from two studies published by the National Center for Health Statistics were used to determine norms (Johnston, Hamill, & Lemeshaw, 1972, 1974). Furthermore, the samples used in the National Center for Health Statistics studies were national probability samples. Thus, the HRPFT norms were based on convenience sample data for three subtests and national probability sample data for the fourth subtest. Third, the HRPFT sample included ages 6 to 17 while the NCYFS measured children and youth in the 10-to-17 age range. Fourth, the testing staff of the NCYF study received extensive formal training at a central site and was monitored closely in the field. Although a training session for HRPFT testers was conducted at a national convention, it is not clear whether all of the testing staff were able to attend. It appears that monitoring of testers was not undertaken in the HRPFT study.

---

[1]The Nabisco/AAU physical fitness program collects fitness data and publishes updated norms annually. Complete tables of norms and information about the fitness program can be obtained from: Nabisco/AAU Physical Fitness Program, 160 HPER Building, Bloomington, IN 47405.

Results

Based on the results of these studies, what can be said about the fitness of American youth? It is difficult to interpret the test scores in an absolute sense. In the past, when field tests of fitness have been administered to children, the interpretation of scores has been relative. That is, a child who can run 1 mile faster than another child is thought to have a higher level of cardiorespiratory function. However, when either child's time on the test is examined, can the score be interpreted in light of the most desirable amount of cardiorespiratory function for that child? This is a more difficult question to answer. For this reason, the NCYFS researchers chose to interpret their data by comparing it with the results of the 1980 HRPFT study. This means that only the HRPFT subtests were compared, since the HRPFT does not include the chin-ups test.

On all four subtests, the 1980 norms were superior to the 1985 norms at almost all ages across both sexes (Pate, Ross, Dotson, & Gilbert, 1985) (see Figures 1-8). For three of the four subtests, the superiority might be explained by the difference in sampling. The rationale behind this explanation is that there is no way of knowing how representative convenience samples are. They may tend to exclude less fit and less motivated students and therefore produce norms that are skewed toward higher performance levels (Pate et al., 1985). However, the fourth subtest, the skinfold measure, could be directly compared since both studies relied upon national probability samples to obtain their skinfold data.

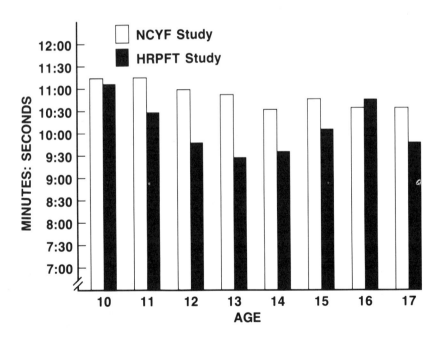

Figure 1—Comparison of 50th-percentile scores for 1-mile run for girls using NCYFS and HRPFT data.

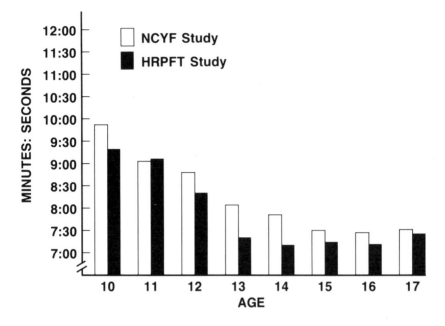

Figure 2—Comparison of 50th-percentile scores for 1-mile run for boys using NCYFS and HRPFT data.

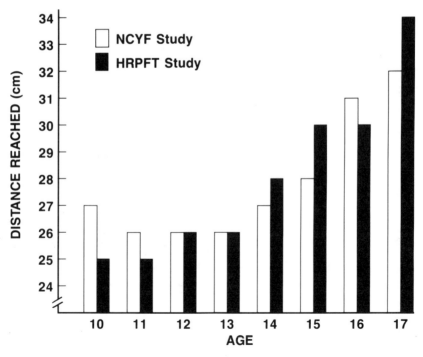

Figure 3—Comparison of 50th-percentile scores for sit-and-reach for boys using NCYFS and HRPFT data.

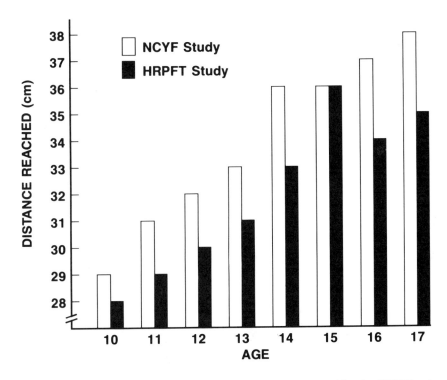

Figure 4—Comparison of 50th-percentile scores for sit-and-reach for girls using NCYFS and HRPFT data.

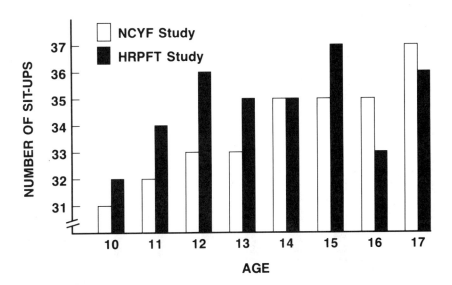

Figure 5—Comparison of 50th-percentile scores for sit-ups for girls using NCYFS and HRPFT data.

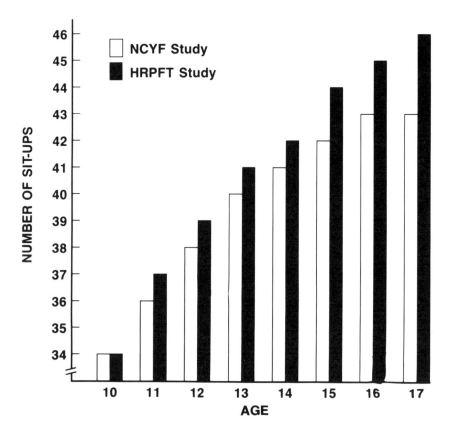

Figure 6—Comparison of 50th-percentile scores for sit-ups for boys using NCYFS and HRPFT data.

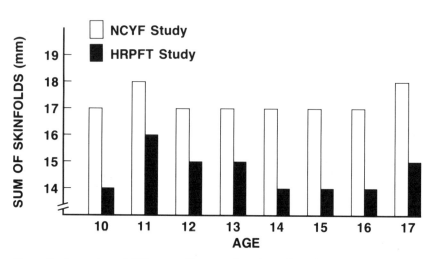

Figure 7—Comparison of 50th-percentile scores for triceps plus subscapular skinfolds for boys using NCYFS and HRPFT data.

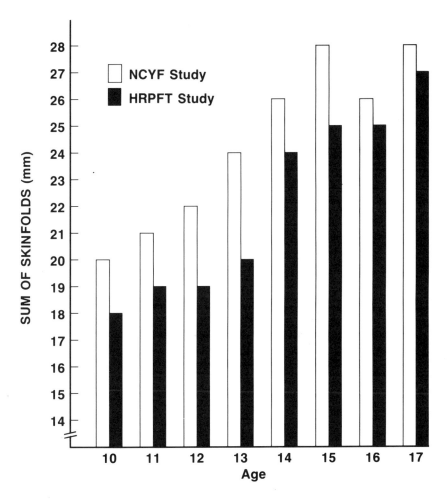

Figure 8—Comparison of 50th-percentile scores for triceps plus subscapular skinfolds for girls using NCYFS and HRPFT data.

Analysis of Skinfold Data

Although comparisons between studies are of primary interest, a brief examination of the NCYFS data provides insight into the distribution of skinfold data. Both the means and medians were reported for each age group by sex. The means were uniformly higher than the medians, as shown in Table 1, indicating that the distributions were skewed. In other words, a small number of extremely heavy children formed the skewed tail of each distribution. The sums of skinfolds, reported in millimeters, were reported to be thicker for children in the 1985 study than in the 1972 and 1974 studies. It was this result of the NCYF study that received considerable attention in newspapers and other forms of the popular press around the country. The general theme was that children today are fatter than they were 10 years ago. Generally these publications reported a 2-3 mm difference in median skinfold sums at each age. The assumption was made that the technique for measuring skinfold thicknesses did not differ in the two studies.

However, this assumption has not been verified and thus is open to question. How meaningful are differences of a magnitude of 2-3 mm, and what were the precise differences in the norms by age and sex? The medians from the HRPFT and NCYF studies are presented in Table 2.

Table 1

Comparison of Means and 50th Percentiles for Sum of Skinfolds
(National Children and Youth Fitness Study, 1985)

Sex	Age							
	10	11	12	13	14	15	16	17
Boys								
M	20.9[a]	21.2	21.6	21.1	20.1	20.1	19.4	20.1
$X_{.50}$	17	18	17	17	17	17	17	17
Girls								
M	22.6	24.8	25.3	26.8	27.9	30.0	28.7	30.2
$X_{.50}$	20	21	22	24	26	28	26	28

[a]Sum of skinfolds expressed in millimeters

Table 2

Comparison of Skinfold Norms from HRPFT and NCYF Studies
(50th Percentile)

Skinfold sites	10	11	12	Age 13	14	15	16	17
Girls								
Triceps plus subscapular								
1972, 1974,	18[a]	19	19	20	24	25	25	27
1985	20	21	22	24	26	28	26	28
Triceps								
1972, 1974	12	12	12	12	14	15	16	16
1985	12	13	13	14	15	16	15	17
Boys								
Triceps plus subscapular								
1972, 1974	14	16	15	15	14	14	14	15
1985	17	18	17	17	17	17	17	17
Triceps								
1972, 1974	9	10	9	9	8	8	8	8
1985	11	11	11	10	9	9	8	8

[a]Sum of skinfolds expressed in millimeters

Note that the differences in the sum of skinfolds for girls range from 1 mm to 4 mm, but the largest difference, 4 mm, occurred only once. For the boys, the differences ranged from 1 mm to 3 mm. Converting these differences to percent body fat using Lohman's formulas (AAHPERD, 1984), a difference of 3 mm represents 2.4% body fat. Specific formulas were developed by Lohman for elementary school-age children. This is a small difference in body fat, even when considering the potential for measurement error. A difference of 1 mm represents less than 1% body fat. This difference has virtually no meaning. On the other hand, the fact that there was a tendency for *all* values to be higher in the 1985 study may have significance. It points to a possible trend in increased body fatness which should be carefully monitored.

Most of these differences were statistically significant. However, since the sample sizes were large, small differences would be detected as statistically significant even though they were not practically significant.

If it is difficult to obtain both the triceps and subscapular skinfold measures, the triceps alone is recommended as an indicator of body fatness. For boys age 14 to 15, the gain in triceps skinfold was 1 mm; for boys age 16 to 17, there was no gain in triceps skinfold. In other words, the 50th percentiles for triceps skinfolds from the 1974 and 1985 studies were exactly the same for the older boys, as shown in Table 2. This suggests that any increase in body fatness occurred at the subscapular site. Exactly the opposite occurred with the older girls. The 1 mm difference in skinfold for 16- to 17-year-old girls can be attributed predominantly to changes in triceps skinfold (see Table 2). This can be explained by the fact that the amount of fat deposited at different sites is differential by sex. In males, there is a tendency to add fat to sites on the trunk, while the female has a greater propensity for depositing fat in the extremities. Keep in mind that all these comparisons have been made at the 50th percentile.

Even though these differences have been identified at the median level of the two studies, this does not mean the same differences were found at higher or lower percentiles. Upper and lower percentiles were examined for both boys and girls, and differ-

Table 3

Comparison of Skinfold Norms from HRPFT and NCYF Studies for Girls at Lower Percentiles

Skinfold			Age		
sites	13	14	15	16	17
25th Percentile					
Triceps plus subscapular					
1974	30	32	34	34	36
1985	31	33	34	33	36
10th Percentile					
Triceps plus subscapular					
1974	43	42	48	46	46
1985	43	40	43	42	42

ences similar to those found at the median were also detected at the 75th and 90th percentiles for both boys and girls, as were differences in the 25th and 10th percentiles for boys. On the other hand, the heavier girls, those at the 25th and 10th percentiles, did not show the same differences in the 10-year comparison, in particular at ages 13 to 17 years. This comparison is shown in Table 3. At the 25th percentile, the sum of skinfolds for girls was similar across the two studies, and sometimes higher in the 1985 study. At the 10th percentile, there was a clear difference in the sum of skinfolds, but sums from the 1985 study were *lower* at every age except 13. Thus, it appears that the heavier girls in 1985 were not as fat as the heavier girls in 1974. Of course, these girls would still be classified as overweight. A sum of skinfolds of 43 mm, for example, represents 33% body fat. A girl with this amount of body fat would clearly be excessively heavy.

Other Trends

Other interesting trends were identified in the NCYFS data. One was the relationship between maturation and test performance (Ross, Dotson, Gilbert, & Katz, 1985b). The results countered the belief that boys' performance on fitness tests tends to peak shortly after puberty and reaches a plateau through age 17, while girls' performance peaks at the onset of puberty and then rapidly declines. The NCYFS data showed that boys increased in abdominal strength, low back flexibility, and upper body strength and decreased in body fatness up to ages 16 and 17. Only in cardiorespiratory function did the performance decline slightly. The girls also continued to improve in abdominal strength and low back flexibility up to ages 16 and 17, but were consistently low in upper body strength as measured by the chin-ups test. Body fatness increased with age, but only to age 15. The girls tended to decline and plateau in cardiorespiratory function after age 14.

The NCYF study, in addition to collecting fitness data, examined the activities included in physical education classes around the country. These results showed that there is a heavy emphasis on relays and informal games for the younger students and on competitive sports for older youth. Although 80% of the students in their sample were enrolled in physical education classes, "there are major problems in the curricula and organizational structure of many physical education programs, especially at the elementary level" (Ross, Dotson, Gilbert, & Katz, 1985c, p. 34). The majority of the students' physical activity time—over 80%—was spent in settings outside the regular physical education class (Ross, Dotson, Gilbert, & Katz, 1985a). Yet the NCYFS investigators estimated that approximately half of American children and youth in grades 5 through 12 did not engage in enough regular, vigorous physical activity on a weekly basis to maintain a healthy cardiorespiratory system (Ross, Dotson, & Gilbert, 1985).

ANALYSIS OF STATUS OF YOUTH FITNESS

Based on the results of the large-scale studies, a substantial proportion of America's children and youth probably do not have an adequate level of fitness. However, comparisons between the NCYFS and HRPFT data seem somewhat tenuous, even for the skinfold measure. Even though these scores differed across age and sex, the difference might be attributable to factors other than skinfold thickness, such as measurement error. Additional research is needed to identify the desired levels of fitness for this age group so that more definitive statements can be made about youth fitness. The time is ripe for implementing sound health-related physical fitness programs in the schools, as this type of fitness is being promoted locally, regionally, and nationally.

For example, in 1980 a report issued by the U.S. Department of Health and Human Services called for improvement in the physical fitness of the nation. This report identified specific objectives in the area of youth fitness. Three objectives are particularly relevant for this paper:

1. By 1990, 60% of American youth will attend physical education classes daily.
2. By 1990, 70% of American youth will periodically have their fitness levels tested.
3. By 1990, 90% of American youth will participate in physical activities that contribute to healthy cardiorespiratory function.

Survey of Physical Education Teachers

A recently completed study (Safrit & Wood, in press) sheds light on the decision-making process leading to the selection of activities that contribute to health-related physical fitness in physical education classes. A survey was conducted in three states to investigate the extent of use of the Health-Related Physical Fitness Test by physical education teachers. The survey took place in 1984, 4 years after the Alliance published the test. A follow-up mailing was implemented but only 31% of the teachers responded. Of the total group of respondents, only 19% were using this test. In the nonuser group, which represented 81% of the respondents, 75% of the teachers had not read or heard of the Health-Related Physical Fitness Test! Yet this test had been publicized extensively on both national and local levels and, in the three states surveyed, presentations had been made at state conventions and workshops. This suggests that a substantial number of physical education teachers do not belong to professional organizations, do not read professional publications, and are not being informed of new developments in physical education. If this is true, means of providing them with updated information ought to be explored.

Whether or not teachers are familiar with a fitness test, schools do not always have the equipment and facilities necessary for fitness testing. In the tri-state survey, one third of the teachers who used the HRPFT did not own a sit-and-reach board and 28% did not own even one inexpensive caliper. In the National Children and Youth Fitness Study, the investigators expected most schools to have a chinning bar, a measured running course, and at least one staff member in physical education familiar with physical fitness testing. However, they soon learned that their expectations could not be met. Some 20% of the schools did not have a chinning bar. Most schools did not own a sit-and-reach board, nor did they have a measured running track. Some did not even have exercise mats. The research team had to provide additional equipment and use specially trained staff far more often than expected. Clearly, equipment for physical fitness assessment is not a high priority in many schools.

To what extent is health-related physical fitness valued in the schools? In the tri-state survey, 11% of the physical education teachers who *used* the health-related test did not feel health-related physical fitness is an important part of the physical education curriculum. Approximately half of them did not feel parents valued health-related fitness, although 70% of the teachers perceived administrators as supportive of this objective. Certainly physical education teachers cannot convince students of the value of fitness if they themselves do not value it. Teachers who *do* value fitness must do more than teach students to value it. As noted in the NCYFS report, "Even if physical educators succeed in conveying the importance of fitness, they may be failing to acquaint students with activities that they can readily perform to stay fit through adulthood" (Ross et al., 1985c, p. 34). It is possible that some physical education teachers are not knowledgeable about the short- and long-term effects of vigorous physical activity and appropriate exercise.

Health-Related Fitness in Early Childhood

Finally, the studies in this paper were focused on children and youth ages 10 to 17. This is not to suggest that health-related physical fitness is not being strongly supported on a national level for early elementary and even for preschool children. The Health-Related Physical Fitness Test has broken new ground by including norms for children ages 6 to 9, and elementary physical education teachers are encouraged to use this test. However, there are many unanswered questions with this age group. As Seefeldt (1984) has noted, we cannot assume that exercise prescriptions and work tolerance which apply to other populations have equal application in early childhood. Not much is known about the interrelationship of physical fitness and overall health in young children. Present knowledge about the cognitive, emotional, and motoric characteristics of young children suggests they are different from other populations.

Some research documents differences between children and adults in their responses to exercise. In two studies, maximal oxygen uptake appeared to account for less variation in children's running performance than has been reported with adults (Costill, Thomason, & Roberts, 1973; Krahenbuhl & Pangrazi, 1983). Seefeldt also pointed out that little information is available concerning the strength, power, or work tolerance of preschool children. These data are difficult to obtain because young children will often refuse to tolerate the discomfort associated with measures such as a stress test.

However, some studies have been conducted on children with reasonable success using laboratory tests of cardiorespiratory function (e.g., DuRant, Dover, & Alpert, 1983; Pels, Gilliam, Freedson, Geenen, & MacConnie, 1981). Another study showed that maximal oxygen uptake can be measured reliably in 10-year-old boys if they reach a plateau in $\dot{V}O_2$ max (Cunningham, Van Waterschoot, Paterson, Lefcoe, & Sangal, 1977). There seems to be no disagreement with the belief that health-related physical fitness should be emphasized in these age groups. To do this well, more information is needed on the physiological parameters of these children under conditions of vigorous physical activity as well as the most effective exercise prescriptions for them.

CONCLUSION

Perhaps the most significant outcome of these studies is that they have highlighted the importance of preparing physical education teachers to incorporate health-related physical fitness concepts and activities into the physical education curriculum. This does not mean fitness should be the sole objective of physical education, but that it should be given proper emphasis in the curriculum. The retraining of physical education teachers who have been in the field for a number of years may be even more important. Bringing teachers up to date on scientific evidence on fitness and its relationship to health is essential. How this can be accomplished in light of budgetary retrenchments is difficult to say. However, our field must accept the challenge to meet a goal that has strong support from our national government and that will yield such obvious benefits for the students we teach and for ourselves.

REFERENCES

AMERICAN Alliance for Health, Physical Education, Recreation, and Dance. (1980). *Health-Related Physical Fitness Test Manual.* Reston, VA: Author.

AMERICAN Alliance for Health, Physical Education, Recreation, and Dance. (1984). *Technical manual: Health-related physical fitness.* Reston, VA: Author.

COSTILL, D.L., Thomason, H., & Roberts, E. (1973). Fractional utilization of aerobic capacity during distance running. *Medicine and Science in Sports, 5,* 258-262.

CUNNINGHAM, D.A., Van Waterschoot, B.M., Paterson, D.H., Lefcoe, M., & Sangal, S.P. (1977). Reliability and reproducibility of maximal oxygen uptake measurement in children. *Medicine and Science in Sports, 9*(2), 104-108.

DuRANT, R.H., Dover, E.V., & Alpert, B.S. (1983). An evaluation of five indices of physical working capacity in children. *Medicine and Science in Sports and Exercise, 15*(1), 83-87.

ERRECART, M.T., Ross, J.G., Gilbert, G.G., & Ghosh, D.N. (1985). Sampling procedures. *Journal of Physical Education, Recreation and Dance, 56*(1), 12-14.

GILLIAM, T.B., Freedson, P.S., MacConnie, S.E., Geenen, D.L., & Pels, A.E. (1981). Comparison of blood lipids, lipoproteins, anthropometric measures, and resting and exercise cardiovascular responses in children 6-7 years old. *Preventive Medicine, 10,* 754-764.

GILLIAM, T.B., Katch, V., Thorland, W., & Weltman, A. (1977). Prevalence of coronary heart disease risk factors in active children, 7 to 12 years of age. *Medicine and Science in Sports, 9,* 21-25.

GILLIAM, T.B., Thorland, W.G., & Sady, S. (1978). Blood lipids and fatness in children age 7-12. *Canadian Journal of Applied Sport Science, 3,* 65-69.

JOHNSTON, F.E., Hamill, D.V., & Lemeshaw, S. (1972). *Skinfold thickness of children 6-11 years* (Series II, No. 120). Washington, DC: U.S. National Center for Health Statistics, U.S. Dept. of HEW.

JOHNSTON, F.E., Hamill, D.V., & Lemeshaw, S. (1974). *Skinfold thickness of youth 12-17 years* (Series II, No. 132). Washington, DC: U.S. National Center for Health Statistics, U.S. Dept. of HEW.

KRAHENBUHL, G.S., & Pangrazi, R.P. (1983). Characteristics associated with running performance in young boys. *Medicine and Science in Sports and Exercise,* **15**(6), 486-490.

PATE, R.R., Ross, J.G., Dotson, C.O., & Gilbert, G.G. (1985). A comparison with the 1980 AAHPERD norms. *Journal of Physical Education, Recreation and Dance,* **56**(1), 28-30.

PELS, A.E., Gilliam, T.B., Freedson, P.S., Geenen, D.L., & MacConnie, S.E. (1981). Heart rate response to bicycle ergometer exercise in children ages 6-7 years. *Medicine and Science in Sports and Exercise,* **13**(5), 299-302.

ROSS, J.G., Dotson, C.O., & Gilbert, G.G. (1985). Are kids getting appropriate activity? *Journal of Physical Education, Recreation and Dance,* **56**(1), 40-43.

ROSS, J.G., Dotson, C.O., Gilbert, G.G., & Katz, S.J. (1985a). After physical education...Physical activity outside of school physical education programs. *Journal of Physical Education, Recreation and Dance,* **56**(1), 35-39.

ROSS, J.G., Dotson, C.O., Gilbert, G.G., & Katz, S.J. (1985b). Maturation and fitness test performance. *Journal of Physical Education, Recreation and Dance,* **56**(1), 20-24.

ROSS, J.G., Dotson, C.O., Gilbert, G.G., & Katz, S.J. (1985c). What are kids doing in school physical education? *Journal of Physical Education, Recreation and Dance,* **56**(1), 31-34.

SAFRIT, M.J., & Wood, T.M. (in press). The Health-Related Physical Fitness Test: A survey of users and nonusers. *Research Quarterly for Exercise and Sport.*

SEEFELDT, V. (1984). Physical fitness in preschool and elementary school-aged children. *Journal of Physical Education, Recreation and Dance,* **55**(9), 33-37, 40.

U.S. Department of Health and Human Services. (1980). *Promoting health/preventing disease: Objectives for the nation.* Washington, DC: Government Printing Office.

WILMORE, J.H., & McNamara, J.J. (1974). Prevalence of coronary disease risk factors in boys, 8-12 years of age. *Journal of Pediatrics,* **84**, 527-533.

PRESIDENTS
American Academy of Physical Education

*1926–30	Clark W. Hetherington
*1930–38	Robert Tait McKenzie
*1938–39	Robert Tait McKenzie
	Mabel Lee
*1939–41	John Brown, Jr.
1941–43	Mabel Lee
*1943–45	Arthur H. Steinhaus
*1945–47	Jay B. Nash
*1947–49	Charles H. McCloy
*1949–50	Frederick W. Cozens
*1950–51	Rosalind Cassidy
1951–52	Seward C. Staley
*1952–53	David K. Brace
1953–54	Neils P. Neilson
1954–55	Elmer D. Mitchell
1955–56	Anna S. Espenschade
*1956–57	Harry A. Scott
*1957–58	Charles C. Cowell
*1958–59	Delbert Oberteuffer
1959–60	Helen Manley
1960–61	Thomas E. McDonough, Sr.
1961–62	M. Gladys Scott
1962–63	Fred V. Hein
1963–64	Carl L. Nordly
*1964–65	Eleanor Metheny
1965–66	Leonard A. Larson
*1966–67	Arthur A. Esslinger
1967–68	Margaret G. Fox
1968–69	Laura J. Huelster
1969–70	H. Harrison Clarke
1970–71	Ruth M. Wilson
1971–72	Ben W. Miller
1972–73	Raymond A. Weiss
1973–74	Ann E. Jewett
1974–75	King J. McCristal
*1975–76	Leona Holbrook
1976–77	Marvin H. Eyler
1977–78	Louis E. Alley
1978–79	Marguerite A. Clifton
1979–80	Harold M. Barrow
1980–81	Aileene S. Lockhart
1981–82	Earle F. Zeigler
1982–83	Edward J. Shea
1983–84	Henry J. Montoye
1984–85	David H. Clarke (current)
1985–86	G. Alan Stull (elect)

*Deceased

With comprehensive coverage of current topics of interest and contributions from the foremost scholars in the field, the Academy Papers are an invaluable resource for every physical education professional and student.

Limits of Human Performance
Volume 18
Edited by David H. Clarke, PhD, and Helen M. Eckert, PhD

In this outstanding collection of papers, Barbara Drinkwater, Hans Lenk, Wayne Sinning, and other scholars provide an intriguing review of how various factors can limit performance. Among the topics addressed are age, psychological influences, morphological and physiological characteristics, heat, biomechanics, and space.

1985 • Paper • 144 pp • Item BCLA0099 • ISBN 0-931250-99-4 • $12.00

Exercise and Health
Volume 17
Edited by Helen M. Eckert, PhD, and Henry J. Montoye, PhD

This timely resource will keep professionals and students abreast of the latest research advances in health and exercise. Charles Tipton, Herbert deVries, Waneen Wyrick Spirduso, and other experts contribute 12 papers examining exercise in relation to coronary heart disease, resting blood pressure, osteoporosis, amenorrhea, obesity, aging, arthritis, mental health, and other factors.

1984 • Paper • 160 pp • Item BECK0056 • ISBN 0-931250-56-0 • $12.00

Human Kinetics Publishers, Inc. • Department 542 • Box 5076
Champaign, IL 61820